Geology of
YELLOWSTONE

A review of the geologic processes and events
responsible for the spectacular natural wonders
of the Yellowstone country.

"* * * and behold! The whole country beyond
was smoking with vapor from boiling springs,
and burning with gases issuing from small
craters, each of which was emitting a sharp,
whistling sound. * * * The general face of the
country was smooth and rolling, being a level
plain, dotted with cone-shaped mounds. On
the summit of these mounds were small
craters from four to six feet in diameter.
Interspersed among these on the level plain
were larger craters, some of them four to six
miles across. Out of these craters, issued blue
flames and molten brimstone."

Description credited to Joseph Meek, 1829; quotation
from page 40 of the book "The Yellowstone National
Park" by Hiram Martin Chittenden (as edited and pub-
lished by Richard A. Bartlett, University of Oklahoma
Press, Norman, Oklahoma, 1964). Photograph is of Midway
Geyser Basin.

"*Be it enacted by the Senate and House of Representatives of the United States of America in Congress assembled,* that the tract of land in the territories of Montana and Wyoming lying near the headwaters of the Yellowstone River is hereby reserved and withdrawn from settlement, occupancy, or sale under the laws of the United States, and dedicated and set apart as a public park or pleasuring ground for the benefit and enjoyment of the people * * *"

Approved March 1, 1872 — signed by:
James G. Blaine, Speaker of the House
Schuyler Colfax, Vice-President of the United States
    and President of the Senate
Ulysses S. Grant, President of the United States

The Geologic Story of

YELLOWSTONE

NATIONAL PARK

By William R. Keefer

Illustrated by John R. Stacy

Based on a planned series of technical re-
ports resulting from comprehensive geologic
studies in Yellowstone National Park by the
author and his colleagues, H. R. Blank, Jr.,
R. L. Christiansen, R. O. Fournier, J. D. Love,
L. J. P. Muffler, J. D. Obradovich, K. L.
Pierce, H. J. Prostka, G. M. Richmond,
Meyer Rubin, E. T. Ruppel, H. W. Smedes,
A. H. Truesdell, H. A. Waldrop, and D. E.
White.

Geological Survey Bulletin 1347

Reprinted by

Yellowstone Library & Museum Assoc.

In Cooperation With

U.S. Geological Survey 1976

Library of Congress catalog-card No. 79-169200

First printing 1971 (1972)

Second printing 1972

Third printing 1976

Fourth printing 1978

Fifth printing 1981

Sixth printing 1984

Foreword

In the aftermath of the Civil War, the United States expanded the exploration of her western frontiers to gain a measure of the vast lands and natural resources in the region now occupied by our Rocky Mountain States. As part of this effort, the Geological and Geographical Survey of the Territories was organized within the Department of the Interior, and staffed by a group of hardy, pioneering scientists under the leadership of geologist F. V. Hayden. During the summer of 1871, these men, accompanied by photographer William H. Jackson and artist Thomas Moran, made a reconnaissance geological study of the legendary and mysterious "Yellowstone Wonderland" in remote northwestern Wyoming Territory. The scientific reports and illustrations prepared by Hayden and his colleagues, supplementing the startling accounts that had been published by members of the famous Washburn-Doane Expedition a year earlier, erased all doubts that this unique land was eminently worthy of being set aside "for the benefit and enjoyment of the people." By Act of Congress on March 1, 1872, our first National Park was established.

During the past century, 50 million people have toured Yellowstone National Park, marveling at its never-ending display of natural wonders. No doubt many have paused to wonder about the origin of these unusual and complex geological features — a question, needless to say, that has intrigued and challenged scientists from the very first days of the Hayden Survey. During the past decade a group of U. S. Geological Survey scientists, in cooperation with the National Park Service and aided by the interest of the National Aeronautics and Space Administration in remote sensing of the geologic phenomena, has been probing the depths and farthest corners of the Park seeking more of the answers. Some of the results of this work, and those of earlier studies, are described in this book to provide a better understanding and enjoyment of this great National Park.

U. E. McKelvey

V. E. McKelvey, Director
U. S. Geological Survey

Contents

Figures

Yellowstone Country

The vivid descriptions brought back from the Yellowstone country by the early explorers and trappers (see frontispiece), whose reputations for telling tall tales were widely accepted if not altogether deserved, fell upon the disbelieving ears of the nation for more than half a century. Yet the intriguing rumors persisted, and during the years 1869-71 several expeditions staffed partly by scientists and engineers rediscovered this unique region atop the backbone of our nation. We now know that the earliest visitors, even if prone to exaggerate, could not do justice to the long-hidden secrets of Yellowstone, for none of them saw all of the fascinating features that occur within this great National Park.

By the time the modern-day visitor enters Yellowstone National Park through any of its five entrances, he probably will have traveled through many parts of the Rocky Mountains and grown somewhat accustomed to the "lay of the land." But this will in no way lessen the exciting impact of viewing the natural wonders of Yellowstone for the first time. Immediate attention, of course, is still drawn to the remarkable array of geysers, hot springs, and other thermal phenomena which in sheer numbers and variety are unsurpassed throughout the world. But, as if these were not enough of an attraction, nature has also provided an incredible setting of sparkling rivers and lakes, thundering waterfalls and cataracts, awesome canyons and gorges, and lofty glaciated mountain peaks and extinct volcanoes. Truly this is a land apart, a spectacular masterpiece of nature that fully deserves the accolade of "wonderland" bestowed long ago by early explorers and trappers. (See figs. 1 and 2.)

1

YELLOWSTONE NATIONAL PARK AREA, showing rivers, lakes, landforms, roads, towns, settlements, and major geyser basins (stippled). The Park embraces 3,472 square miles (2,221,770 acres), and its boundaries traverse a distance of nearly 300 miles. Yellowstone Lake, with an irregular shoreline of 110 miles and a surface area of 137 square miles, is one of the largest natural mountain lakes in the United States. (Fig. 1)

2

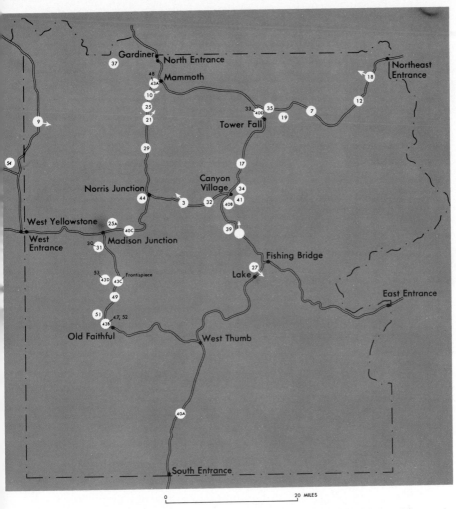

INDEX MAP showing localities where photographs (and one sketch, fig. 35) were taken to illustrate this bulletin. For photographs of distant views, arrows point in direction of view. Numbers refer to figure numbers in text. (Fig. 2)

Beyond the first stirring impressions derived from the grandeur of the vast Yellowstone wilderness and its myriad wildlife, assuredly shared by people of all ages and from all walks of life, the various aspects of the Park take on a very different meaning for different individuals. The artist sees grand vistas to be painted, the naturalist delights in the flower-laden meadows and the native habitats of many kinds of birds and animals, the engineer visualizes the amount of energy stored in the waterfalls and steaming geysers, and so on. To the geologist, in particular, who studies rocks and fossils and all of the natural processes involved in shaping the surface of the land, and to all those who would share such interests, Yellowstone takes on a very special meaning. For the Park is foremost a geological Park, created by an extraordinary sequence of natural processes and events that have combined to produce an immense outdoor laboratory for studies that have contributed to a fuller knowledge and a better understanding of the earth itself. The geological aspect of the Yellowstone country is reflected by its very name, given long ago to the river that issues from the great canyon of the "yellow rocks." [1] This report, borrowing from a century of scientific study within and around the Park area, describes the geological "how, why, and when" of this unique and fascinating region.

A geological preview

Some 600,000 years ago the rumblings of an impending volcanic eruption sounded ominously across the Yellowstone country. Suddenly, in a mighty crescendo of deafening explosions, tremendous quantities of hot volcanic ash and pumice spewed from giant cracks at the earth's surface. Towering dust clouds blackened the sky, and vast sheets of volcanic debris spread out rapidly across the countryside in all directions, covering thousands of square miles in a matter of minutes with a blanket of utter devastation. Abruptly, a great smoldering pit — a caldera 30 miles across, 45 miles long, and several thousand feet deep — appeared in the central Yellowstone region, the ground having fallen into the huge underground cavern that was left by the earth-shaking eruptions. Lava then began oozing from the cracks to fill the still-smoking caldera.

---

[1] The specific area about which the early-day Indians first used the term that is now translated as "Yellowstone" is unknown. The name may have referred to the yellowish rocks that line the banks of the Yellowstone River near its confluence with the Missouri River in eastern Montana and western North Dakota. However, in the opinion of H. M. Chittenden, who studied the question in considerable detail, there is little doubt that the name was taken from the striking yellow-hued walls of the gorge now known as the Grand Canyon of the Yellowstone.

Thus, in one brief "moment" of geologic time there was launched that incredible chain of events which led to the creation of many of the natural wonders of Yellowstone National Park. Heat from the enormous reservoir of molten rock which produced the massive eruption still remains deep within the earth beneath Yellowstone, sustaining the spectacular hot-water and steam phenomena for which the Park is so justly famous. The formation of the caldera and the eruption of lavas profoundly influenced the shape of the present-day landscape. Once a land covered almost entirely by mountains, the part that collapsed — nearly one-third of the total Park area — is now characterized by low rolling plateaus formed from the thick lava flows that filled the caldera (figs. 1 and 2; see fig. 22 for the outline of the Yellowstone caldera). Moreover, the carving of the spectacular Grand Canyon of the Yellowstone (fig. 41) and the fashioning of the large interior basin now occupied by beautiful Yellowstone Lake (fig. 27) were closely related to this mighty volcanic event.

North, east, and south of the central plateaus are extensive mountain ranges and other highlands which provide much of the Park's scenic beauty (figs. 3 and 4). Formed by many episodes of intense mountain building and ancient volcanism, these uplands bear the lasting imprints of a wide variety of geological activities that date back approximately 2.7 billion years. Indeed, as we study all the features of the Yellowstone landscape, we find in them a most impressive and fascinating story of that ageless conflict between the internal forces of nature that raise the land through the upheaval of mountains and the eruption of volcanoes, and the external forces of erosion that wear the land down. It is this vast relentless interplay of giant forces that determines the appearance of any given place upon the earth's surface. And, in few other places around the globe can the processes of both building up and tearing down the landscape be illustrated more dramatically than in Yellowstone National Park.

SKYLINE OF THE GALLATIN RANGE in northwestern Yellowstone National Park, as viewed from a point on the road between Canyon Village and Norris Junction. The range consists chiefly of Paleozoic and Mesozoic sedimentary rocks and Precambrian metamorphic rocks that were uplifted by folding and faulting of the earth's crust. The dark-gray rocks along the roadcut in the left foreground are rhyolite lava flows of the Solfatara Plateau. (Fig. 3)

The nature of the rocks reveals their origins

Geologists believe that "the present is the key to the past." After observing lava erupting from a present-day volcano or limestone forming in marine waters, we infer that similar types of ancient lavas or ancient limestones formed in virtually the same ways. This kind of reasoning is used to interpret the origins of all types of ancient rocks, for all the known geological processes that form rocks seem to have been operating since the earth's beginning.

Figure 5 shows the many different rock units that have been recognized in Yellowstone National Park. Arranged in a vertical column according to the geologic time intervals in which they formed, these rocks represent a large part of total earth history (fig. 6). A generalized geologic map (plate 1) shows the distribution of the various units (or groups of closely related units) exposed at the surface throughout the Park area. This map and figure 5 summarize much of the information that is necessary to interpret the Park's geologic history — in essence, to provide answers to these two important questions: What were the geologic events that formed the rocks? When did these events occur?

The oldest rocks

If we were to walk backward in time at the rate of one century per step, the first step would return us to 1872, the year that Yellowstone National Park was established. But to return to the oldest recorded event in its geologic history,

◁ HAYDEN VALLEY. View north along the Yellowstone River and Hayden Valley toward the Washburn Range. Mount Washburn, part of an ancient Absaroka volcano, is the highest prominence (elevation, 10,293 feet) on the skyline to the right, and Dunraven Pass is in the notch in the center of the skyline. The foot of the range marks the north edge of the Yellowstone caldera. Hayden Valley is cut in glacial lake sediments that overlie thick lava flows covering the caldera floor. (Fig. 4)

7

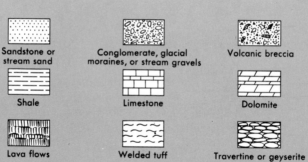

AGE, IN THOUSANDS OF YEARS	ROCK FORMATION OR UNIT	
40± to present 9 to 250±	Stream sand and gravel Hot-spring deposits Glacial deposits	
60 to 600	Plateau Rhyolite	
600	Upper Unit, Yellowstone Tuff	
600 to 2,000	Rhyolite and basalt lava flows	
2,000	Lower Unit, Yellowstone Tuff	
2,000 +	Rhyolite and basalt lava flows	

Sandstone or stream sand

Conglomerate, glacial moraines, or stream gravels

Volcanic breccia

Shale

Limestone

Dolomite

Lava flows

Welded tuff

Travertine or geyserite

KINDS OF ROCKS SHOWN IN COLUMNS

THE ROCKS of Yellowstone National Park, separated into individual units or formations and arranged according to their geologic ages (see fig. 6). A formation is a body of rock that contains certain identifying features (such as composition, color, and fossils) which set it apart from all other rock units. The identifying features of each formation provide valuable clues bearing on its origin. Most formations are given formal names, and usually each formation is thick and widespread enough to be recognized over broad areas. Some, however, change character from place to place, and different names may be used in different areas even though the rocks represent the same geologic time interval. (Fig. 5)

ROCK FORMATIONS		AGE, IN MILLIONS OF YEARS	PERIOD	ERA
Northern part of park	Southern part of park			
Thick lava flows, welded tuffs, glacial deposits, and hot-spring deposits		2–3	QUATERNARY	CENOZOIC
Pliocene, Miocene, and Oligocene rocks not known to be present		37–38		
Absaroka volcanic rocks	Absaroka volcanic rocks (Eocene)		TERTIARY	
		53–54		
Volcanic and sedimentary rocks (largely eroded away before Absaroka volcanic rocks were deposited)	Pinyon Conglomerate (Paleocene and Cretaceous)	65		MESOZOIC
Landslide Creek Formation	Harebell Formation		CRETACEOUS	
Everts Formation	(Eroded away before Harebell was deposited)			
Eagle Sandstone	Bacon Ridge Sandstone			
Telegraph Creek Fm				
Cody Shale	Cody Shale			
Frontier Formation	Frontier Formation			
Mowry Shale	Mowry Shale			
Thermopolis Shale	Thermopolis Shale			
Kootenai Formation	Cloverly Formation	136		
Morrison Formation	Morrison(?) Formation			
Swift Formation	Sundance Formation		JURASSIC	
Rierdon Formation				
Sawtooth Formation	Gypsum Spring Fm	190–195		
Woodside & Thaynes(?) Formations	Chugwater Formation		TRIASSIC	
Dinwoody Formation	Dinwoody Formation	225		
Shedhorn Sandstone	Phosphoria Fm and related rocks	280	PERMIAN	PALEOZOIC
Quadrant Sandstone	Tensleep Formation		PENNSYLVANIAN	
Amsden Formation	Amsden Formation			
Mission Canyon Limestone	Madison Limestone		MISSISSIPPIAN	
Lodgepole Limestone		345		
Three Forks Formation	Darby Formation		DEVONIAN	
Jefferson Formation				
Bighorn Dolomite		500	ORDOVICIAN	
Snowy Range Fm	(Not exposed, except for isolated outcrops of some formations in Falls River area, in southwestern part of park)			
Pilgrim Limestone			CAMBRIAN	
Park Shale				
Meagher Limestone				
Wolsey Shale				
Flathead Sandstone		570		
Gneiss and Schist	(Not exposed)	2,700	PRECAMBRIAN	

Approx. scale in feet: 0 1,000 2,000 3,000

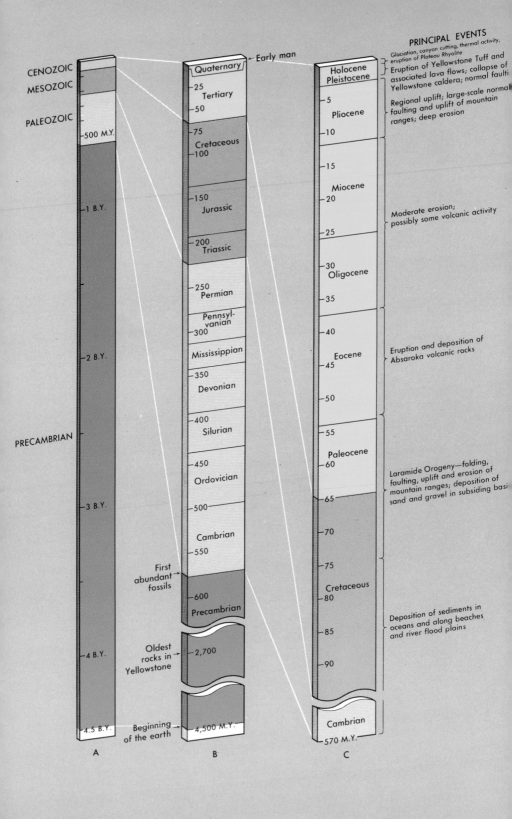

PRINCIPAL EVENTS

Glaciation, canyon cutting, thermal activity, eruption of Plateau Rhyolite

Eruption of Yellowstone Tuff and associated lava flows; collapse of Yellowstone caldera; normal faulti

Regional uplift; large-scale normal faulting and uplift of mountain ranges; deep erosion

Moderate erosion; possibly some volcanic activity

Eruption and deposition of Absaroka volcanic rocks

Laramide Orogeny—folding, faulting, uplift and erosion of mountain ranges; deposition of sand and gravel in subsiding basi

Deposition of sediments in oceans and along beaches and river flood plains

CENOZOIC
MESOZOIC
PALEOZOIC

-500 M.Y.

-1 B.Y.

-2 B.Y.

PRECAMBRIAN

-3 B.Y.

-4 B.Y.

-4.5 B.Y.

A

Early man

Quaternary
-25 Tertiary
-50
-75 Cretaceous
-100
-150 Jurassic
-200 Triassic
-250 Permian
Pennsyl-vanian
-300
Mississippian
-350
Devonian
-400
Silurian
-450
Ordovician
-500
Cambrian
-550

First abundant fossils

-600
Precambrian

Oldest rocks in Yellowstone

-2,700

Beginning of the earth

-4,500 M.Y.

B

Holocene
Pleistocene
-5 Pliocene
-10
-15
Miocene
-20
-25
-30 Oligocene
-35
-40
Eocene
-45
-50
-55
Paleocene
-60
-65
-70
-75
Cretaceous
-80
-85
-90

Cambrian
-570 M.Y.

C

◁ THE GEOLOGIC TIME SCALE — the "calendar" used by geologists in interpreting earth history. Column A, graduated in billions of years (B.Y.) and subdivided into the four major geologic eras (Precambrian, for example), represents the time elapsed since the beginning of the earth, which is believed to have been about 4.5 billion years ago. Column B is an expansion of part of the time scale in millions of years (M.Y.), to show the subdivisions (periods — Cambrian, for example) of the Paleozoic, Mesozoic, and Cenozoic Eras; column C is a further expansion to show particularly the subdivisions (epochs — Paleocene, for example) of the Tertiary and Quaternary Periods. The principal events in the geologic history of Yellowstone National Park are listed to the right of column C, opposite the time intervals in which they occurred. The ages, in years, are based on radiometric dating. Many rocks contain radioactive elements which begin to decay at a very slow but measurable rate as soon as the parent rock is formed. The most common radioactive elements are uranium, rubidium, and potassium, and their decay ("daughter") products are lead, strontium, and argon, respectively. By measuring both the amount of a given daughter product and the amount of the original radioactive element still remaining in the parent rock, and then relating these measurements to their known rate of radioactive decay, the age of the rock in actual numbers of years can be calculated. The decay of radioactive carbon (carbon-14) to nitrogen is especially useful for dating rocks less than 40,000 years old. (Fig. 6)

we would have to walk (at 3 feet per step) some 15,000 miles, or three-fifths of the way around the world! Occurring far back in the antiquity of the Precambrian Era—approximately 2.7 billion years ago according to radiometric dating (fig. 6) — the oldest event resulted in rocks so crumpled and changed by heat and pressure that their original character is obscure. These rocks, having been transformed from still older ones, are called *metamorphic rocks.* Considered to form part of the very foundation of the continent itself, they are also commonly referred to as *basement rocks.*

Gneiss, a coarsely banded rock (fig. 7), and schist, a finely banded rock, are the most common kinds of metamorphic rocks in Yellowstone. Originally, the gneiss probably was granite, and the schist was a shale or sandstone. Outcrops of the gneisses and schists occur only in the northern part of the Park (pl. 1), where they form the central cores of some mountain ranges such as the Gallatin Range (fig. 3). They also lie buried beneath younger rocks in many other areas of the Park.

From the time of the metamorphic event, when the gneisses and schists were formed, until the deposition of sediments of the Cambrian Period (figs. 5 and 6), there is virtually no record. It is reasonably certain, however, that several times during this 2.1-billion-year interval the region was intensely squeezed and uplifted into high mountains and then

11

├─1 INCH─┤

deeply eroded. By the end of Precambrian time, approximately 570 million years ago, the ancient Yellowstone landscape had been reduced by erosion to a flat, stark, almost featureless plain, which was soon to be flooded by a shallow sea encroaching from the west. This very old surface is now partly exposed in some places across the Buffalo Plateau, at the north edge of the Park (fig. 1).

The deposits of the shifting seas

From the appearance of the rugged, mountainous terrain of Yellowstone National Park, it is difficult to visualize a time when this region lay close to sea level, at times even below sea level. Yet the evidence is clear that from the Cambrian Period to the latter part of the Cretaceous Period, a span of about 500 million years, vast stretches of western lands were flooded repeatedly by broad shallow seas that often reached from Canada to Mexico (fig. 8). During these great floodings, widespread horizontal beds of sand, silt, clay, limy mud, and other sediments were deposited on the ocean floors, along the adjoining beaches and wide tidal flats, and across the broad flood plains of large rivers that emptied into the seas. All of these ancient sediments have now hardened into compact well-layered sandstones, shales, and limestones (figs. 9 and 10). These *sedimentary rocks* have been divided into 25 or more distinct formations in the Yellowstone region (fig. 5), where they locally attain a combined thickness of more than 10,000 feet.

The first Paleozoic sea to reach the Yellowstone region, some 550 million years ago, brought with it the earliest abundant signs of life on earth. Small hard-shelled animals that lived mainly on the shallow sea bottom are now preserved as fossils in rocks deposited during the Cambrian Period. Many of these animals were *trilobites,* long-extinct organisms resembling today's crabs and spiders. Each younger set of rocks or formations contains a different group of dominant fossils, each diagnostic of that period of geologic time in which they lived (fig. 11).

◁ LAMAR RIVER. View downstream (west) along the Lamar River in Lamar Canyon. The rocks along the river banks are coarsely banded Precambrian gneisses more than 2.5 billion years old, some of the oldest rocks in Yellowstone National Park. Closeup views show coarse banding and texture of the gneiss; minerals include quartz, feldspar, and biotite (black mica). (Fig. 7)

13

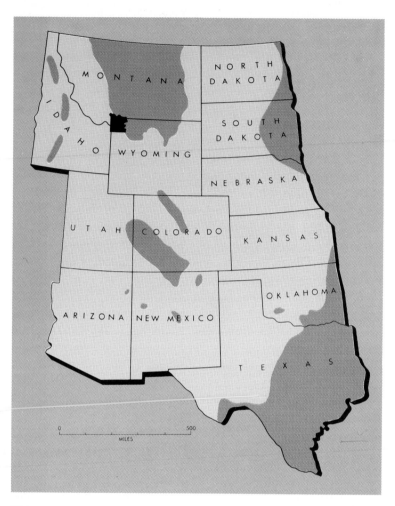

MIDDLE PERMIAN SEAS. Distribution of sea (blue) and land (red) during the middle part of Permian time (approximately 250 million years ago). Only a part of the Yellowstone National Park area (black) was flooded during this period. (Fig. 8)

CROWFOOT RIDGE in the southern Gallatin Range, as viewed from the road along the ▷ Gallatin River near the northwest corner of Yellowstone National Park. The rocks, chiefly Paleozoic limestone, sandstone, and shale, were deposited in broad shallow seas that covered all of the Yellowstone region several hundred million years ago. The original layers were horizontal, but they have since been tilted and broken by giant mountain-building forces originating deep within the earth. (Fig. 9)

14

Fossils indicate the kind of environment in which the animals lived (fig. 12). Some species thrived in the open oceans; others thrived only along the beaches and in nearby lagoons. Still others, such as the incredibly large dinosaurs of the Jurassic and Cretaceous Periods, could survive only on the land or in swamps. From studies of the fossils and of the physical characteristics of the rocks in which they are now found, the shoreline patterns of the shifting seas can be determined. Studies show that the seas advanced and retreated across the Yellowstone Park region at least a dozen times during the Paleozoic and Mesozoic Eras.

Toward the end of the Mesozoic Era (in the latter part of the Cretaceous Period), the metamorphic basement rocks of Yellowstone lay covered by the vast blanket of flat-lying sediments. Today, these sedimentary rocks are exposed along the Snake River and its tributaries in the south-central part of the Park, over much of the Gallatin Range in the northwest corner, and at several places in the north-central and northeastern parts (pl. 1). Elsewhere, either they are hidden from view beneath volcanic debris — ash and lava — that later buried them, or they have been removed by erosion. But wherever exposed, the original horizontal layers of sedimentary rocks have been severely twisted and broken by later mountain-building movements.

MOUNT EVERTS, as viewed toward the northeast from the road south of Mammoth Hot Springs. The mountain, about 1,500 feet high above the plain, is formed by gently tilted sedimentary rocks of Cretaceous age, chiefly sandstone and shale of the Frontier, Cody, and Everts Formations (fig. 5). The conspicuous rimrock at the top of the mountain to the right is composed of the Yellowstone Tuff. When the tuff was deposited (by explosive eruptions from the south), there was no valley along the edge of the mountain. (Fig. 10)

FAUNAL SUCCESSION in sedimentary rocks. The different animals are now preserved ▷ as fossils, which are diagnostic of the period in which the animals lived. (Fig. 11)

16

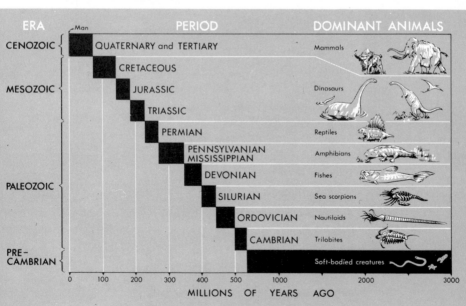

ERA	Man	PERIOD	DOMINANT ANIMALS	
CENOZOIC {		QUATERNARY and TERTIARY	Mammals	
MESOZOIC {		CRETACEOUS		
		JURASSIC	Dinosaurs	
		TRIASSIC		
PALEOZOIC {		PERMIAN	Reptiles	
		PENNSYLVANIAN MISSISSIPPIAN	Amphibians	
		DEVONIAN	Fishes	
		SILURIAN	Sea scorpions	
		ORDOVICIAN	Nautiloids	
		CAMBRIAN	Trilobites	
PRE- CAMBRIAN {			Soft-bodied creatures	

0   100   200   300   400   500   1000   2000   3000

MILLIONS OF YEARS AGO

A

B

├─1 INCH─┤

The first mountain-building episode

Near the close of the Mesozoic Era the earth was subjected to a series of intense crustal disturbances that geologists call the Laramide orogeny (orogeny means mountain-building). The origin and nature of the forces that bent and cracked the crust are unknown, but current theories being developed about sea-floor spreading and continental drift may shed light on this major upheaval that began about 75 million years ago. A significant effect of the Laramide orogeny was the uplift and contortion of many of the mountain ranges within what we today call the Rocky Mountains.

At the onset of the crustal disturbance, the gently rolling landscape of the Yellowstone region began to warp and flex into large upfolds (*anticlines*) and downfolds (*synclines*) (fig. 13). Gradually the mountain-building pressures increased, finally reaching such magnitude that the limbs of the folds could bend and stretch no further; thereupon, the rock layers broke and were shoved over one another along extensive *reverse faults*. The severely crumpled rocks within the Park area can now be seen only along the north edge and in the south-central part along the Snake River. In both places, the folds and faults are especially well displayed by the layered Paleozoic and Mesozoic sedimentary formations (fig. 9).

One of the most prominent Laramide structural features is a large anticline in the north-central and northeastern parts of the Park (fig. 14, section B–B'); the road from Mammoth to the Northeast Entrance crosses much of this feature (pl. 1). Although originally forming a high mountain mass, the anticline has been eroded so extensively that it no longer appears mountainous (fig. 18). It displays a broad core of Precambrian gneisses and schists and is bounded along its southwest margin by a large reverse fault. Along the fault, the ancient gneisses and schists have been shoved over rocks as young as Late Cretaceous, a movement amounting to

◁ LIMESTONE OF MISSISSIPPIAN AGE along Pebble Creek at the Pebble Creek campground, northeastern Yellowstone National Park. Closeup A shows one of the highly fossiliferous layers within the limestone, and closeup B shows some of the fossils and their casts. Most of the fossils are of a variety of shelled sea animals (brachiopods) that lived on the ocean floors approximately 300 million years ago. (Fig. 12)

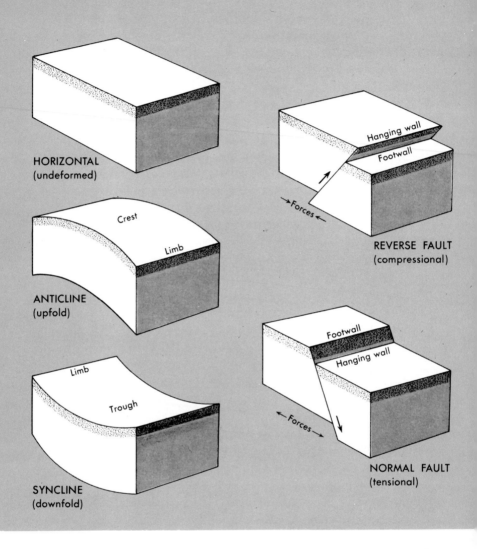

HORIZONTAL
(undeformed)

Hanging wall

Footwall

→Forces←

REVERSE FAULT
(compressional)

Crest

Limb

ANTICLINE
(upfold)

Footwall

Hanging wall

←Forces→

Limb

Trough

NORMAL FAULT
(tensional)

SYNCLINE
(downfold)

COMMON KINDS OF GEOLOGIC STRUCTURES produced by deformation of the earth's crust. An original horizontal rock layer may be upfolded into anticlines, downfolded into synclines, and broken by either reverse or normal faults. A fault is a fracture or a zone of fractures within the earth's crust along which movement has taken place. A reverse fault is one generally produced by compression (squeezing together), and the hanging-wall block has moved up with respect to the footwall block. A normal fault is one generally produced by tension (pulling apart), and the hanging-wall block has moved down with respect to the footwall block. All these kinds of structures are present in Yellowstone National Park. (Fig. 13)

10,000 feet or more. The Cretaceous rocks are those that are now exposed at Mount Everts (fig. 10).

During the Laramide orogeny, many folds and faults formed in the northwestern part of the Park, in the area now occupied by the Gallatin Range (fig. 14, section A–A'). In south-central Yellowstone, the Paleozoic and Mesozoic sedimentary rocks were tightly folded into three anticlines separated from one another by synclines and faults (fig. 14, section C–C'). Movement along one reverse fault in this area was locally more than 10,000 feet.

As the lands were uplifted and contorted, they came under vigorous attack by the ever-present agents of erosion. Tremendous quantities of rock were stripped from the highlands, and the debris was carried by streams into the adjacent lowland basins and deposited mostly as sand and gravel. As the highlands continued to rise, the basins continued to sink, and in a short period of time great thicknesses of basin-fill sediments accumulated locally. One such deposit, the Harebell Formation of latest Cretaceous age in south-central Yellowstone (fig. 5), is more than 8,000 feet thick.

Other similar anticlines, synclines, and reverse faults no doubt extend far into the interior of Yellowstone National Park, and perhaps entirely across it in places, but they lie buried beneath a thick capping of volcanic rocks. Nevertheless, it seems safe to conclude that none of the Park area escaped the effects of the great forces of the Laramide orogeny. These forces, regardless of how they originated deep within the earth, seem to have been compressional (fig. 13), pushing the upper layers of the earth's crust from the east and northeast toward the west and southwest. This interpretation is based on the style of the structural features just described, which shows that the steep limbs of folds, as well as the direction of movements along reverse faults, point toward the west or southwest (fig. 14).

By early Eocene time, about 20 million years after they had begun, the deformational forces relaxed. But the effects of the giant earth movements were to last for a very long time. Crustal disturbances of such magnitude commonly produce conditions deep within the earth which, in places, gives rise to intense volcanic activity; one such place was Yellowstone.

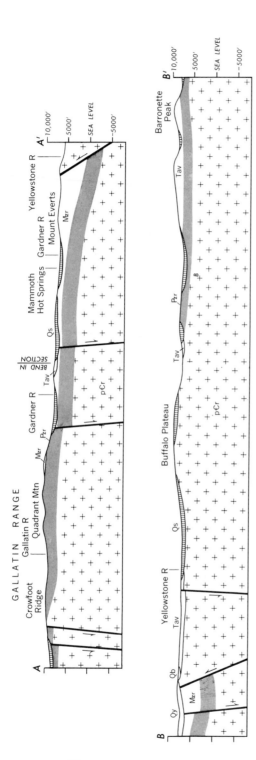

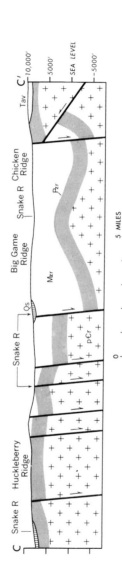

CROSS SECTIONS SHOWING GEOLOGIC STRUCTURES in Yellowstone National Park. These illustrate the possible rock relationships that might be seen along the faces of vertical slices of the earth's crust, if it could be cut and pulled apart (much like slicing a cake and looking at the different layers). The locations of the sections are shown on the geologic map, plate 1. Reverse faults and most folds originated during the Laramide orogeny, and normal faults originated chiefly during Pliocene and later times. The arrows indicate the relative movements of fault blocks. Geologic symbols: Qs, Quaternary surficial deposits; Qb, Quaternary basalt flows; Qy, Quaternary Yellowstone Tuff; Tav, Tertiary Absaroka volcanic rocks; Mzr, Mesozoic sedimentary rocks; Pzr, Paleozoic sedimentary rocks; p€r, Precambrian metamorphic ("basement") rocks. (Based partly on information supplied by E.T. Ruppel and J.D. Love.)(Fig. 14)

22

Volcanic activity

In early Eocene time, between 55 and 50 million years ago, several large volcanoes erupted in and near Yellowstone National Park. This volcanic activity resulted in the accumulation of the vast pile of Absaroka volcanic rocks (fig. 5) which now makes up most of the Absaroka and Washburn Ranges and part of the Gallatin Range, and which covers several other smaller areas in the Park (pl. 1).

What special geologic conditions would cause these spectacular eruptions of molten rock at the earth's surface? Measurements taken in deep mines and oil wells show that the normal increase in the earth's temperature with depth is about 1°F per 100 feet. This heat is generated by the decay of radioactive elements — chiefly uranium, thorium, and potassium — which are present in at least small amounts in virtually all rocks of the earth's crust. Ordinarily, enough heat is conducted to the earth's surface so that the deeply buried rocks do not become hot enough to melt. In some places, however, the heat is not carried off fast enough, and the temperature rises slowly toward the melting point of the rock. Such hot spots may develop (1) because the rocks in those places contain more than an average amount of radioactive elements; (2) because hotter material moves upward from still deeper levels in the earth; or (3) because drastic changes in pressure are brought about by the alternate squeezing and relaxing of mountain-building forces, which in turn substantially affect the melting point of the rocks. Whatever the cause, the eventual result is the accumulation of a huge body of molten rock, called *magma,* enclosed in a deep underground chamber.

Magma, being a mixture of hot liquids and gases that is lighter in weight than the solid rocks surrounding it, tends to rise toward the earth's surface. Forcing its way upward, some of the molten material solidifies before reaching the surface and forms bodies of various kinds of *intrusive igneous rocks* (fig. 15). Some of the magma, however, reaches the surface and either pours out as lava or is blown out explosively as rock fragments, ash, and pumice to form *extrusive igneous rocks.*

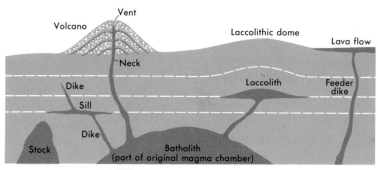

Rock name	Principal rock-forming minerals	Color
Rhyolite ... Quartz,[1] feldspar[2] (sanidine).		Light to medium shades of gray and brown.
Andesite ... Feldspar[2] (plagioclase), pyroxene[3] (augite).		Medium to fairly dark shades of brown, red, purple, and gray.
Basalt ... Feldspar (plagioclase), pyroxene, olivine,[3] magnetite.[4]		Nearly black.

[1] Clear to light-colored silicon dioxide.
[2] Light-colored aluminum silicate minerals.
[3] Dark-colored iron and magnesium silicate minerals.
[4] Very dark colored iron oxide mineral.

INTRUSIVE AND EXTRUSIVE IGNEOUS ROCK BODIES. Extrusive rocks solidified above ground, and intrusive rocks solidified below ground. All features shown occur in Yellowstone National Park. Extrusive rocks are the predominant rock type seen along the Park roads, and the table above lists the three principal kinds that are present. (Fig. 15)

The magmas which formed the Absaroka volcanoes erupted mainly through large central vents (fig. 16). Most of the eruptions were fairly quiet, with the molten rock welling up to the surface and cascading down the sides of the volcanoes chiefly as viscous lava flows and breccias. Rain, seeping into these porous rocks, caused huge landslides of mud and broken rock to stream down the mountainsides. Hence, many of the rocks seen today are volcanic breccias — jumbled but crudely layered deposits of large and small angular blocks embedded in a sandy matrix, much like man-made concrete except that the rock fragments are considerably coarser (fig. 17). Viewed from a distance, however, most of the breccia deposits have a distinct layered appearance (fig. 18). The predominant extrusive igneous rock in the Absaroka volcanic sequence is andesite, but basalt also occurs in places (fig. 15).

24

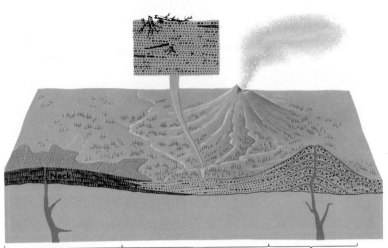

| Chiefly lava flows of shield volcano | Chiefly volcanic sandstone and conglomerate of lowland areas | Chiefly volcanic breccias and thin lava flows of cone-type volcano |

ABSAROKA VOLCANOES and their rocks. Lava (mostly andesite) poured from central vents and formed volcanoes, some steep sided and others broad and relatively flat. As the lava spilled out, much of it quickly solidified, broke up into large angular blocks (breccia), and then either tumbled down the slopes of the volcanoes as individual boulders or slid down in mudflows and landslides. Some of the material was also explosively blown out as rock bombs, cinders, and ash. The more fluid lava (mostly basalt), on the other hand, flowed quietly down the volcanic slopes and onto the surrounding lowlands. The rocks near the volcanic centers therefore include thick crudely layered coarse breccias, thin fine ash and dust falls, and thin to thick lava flows. The volcanoes were repeatedly attacked by erosion, and the eroded material was redeposited by streams and mudflows in widespread layers of volcanic conglomerate and sandstone across the flat-floored valleys and plains between the volcanoes. Forests, which grew luxuriantly in these lowland areas, were repeatedly buried by volcanic eruptions and are now preserved (see inset) as the fossil forests of Yellowstone. (Based on information supplied by H. W. Smedes and H. J. Prostka.) (Fig. 16)

At times the Absaroka volcanic eruptions were violently explosive, showering the countryside with rock bombs, cinders, and ash. The finer debris that reached the lower slopes of the volcanoes was reworked and carried by streams into the intervening valleys, where it was deposited as sand and gravel (fig. 16). Eventually the entire Yellowstone region was choked with volcanic debris, the material from one volcano mixing with that from neighboring volcanoes. Even the mountain masses uplifted during the preceding Laramide orogeny were covered by the vast accumulation (fig. 18).

Absaroka volcanism, however, was not a simple, continuous process — the eruptions were intermittent, the many

25

volcanoes were not always active at the same time, and between eruptions there were long periods of quiescence during which the erupted material was deeply eroded. The repetitive nature of the eruptions is best illustrated by the famous fossil forests of Yellowstone. Here is striking evidence that enough time elapsed between eruptions for widespread forests to become established on the lower slopes of the volcanoes and in the broad valleys between them. Judged from the great size of some of the now-petrified logs (fig. 19), several hundreds of years must have passed before another volcanic outburst smothered the forest. Many different forest layers have been recognized in the Specimen Ridge area as well as in several other places throughout the Park.

As the Absaroka magma rose from deep underground, some of it squirted, like toothpaste, into the layered Paleozoic and Mesozoic sedimentary rocks through which it passed. These relatively small masses of molten rock material slowly cooled and crystallized to form intrusive igneous rocks such as diorite (fig. 20). The resulting intrusive bodies, called *sills, dikes, stocks,* and *laccoliths,* depending on their form, are most abundant in the Gallatin Range and in the vicinity of the East Entrance (pl. 1). At the conclusion of volcanic activity, the last of the rising magma solidified in the main conduits to form slender, somewhat cylindrical bodies of rock called *volcanic necks* that probably conform closely to the shape of the original conduits. The circular intrusive rock body at Bunsen Peak (fig. 21), now exposed to view because erosion has stripped away the lava and volcanic breccia that once completely buried it, represents either a volcanic neck or a small stock that solidified directly beneath a volcano.

Mount Washburn is the north half of one of the ancient Absaroka volcanoes (fig. 26), and many of the rocks and other features related to this volcano, which characterized this great period of volcanism, can be seen along the road between Canyon Village and Tower. In roadcuts just south

◁ MASSIVE BEDS OF BRECCIA of the Absaroka volcanic rocks along the road north of Dunraven Pass. This breccia formed part of a steep-sided volcanic cone, of which Mount Washburn is a remnant. Closeup view shows very coarse character of the breccia, with large rock fragments imbedded in fine ash, dust, and sand. Nearly all the rocks are of andesitic composition, consisting chiefly of feldspar and pyroxene. Most common colors are medium to fairly dark shades of brown, red, purple, and gray. (Fig. 17)

ABSAROKA

PALEOZOIC

MASSIVELY LAYERED BRECCIAS, conglomerates, and sandstones of the Absaroka volcanic sequence at Barronette Peak, as viewed from the road near the Northeast
Entrance; the ridge is 3,000 feet high. These rocks, deposited as part of an alluvial
plain between volcanoes, once filled the Yellowstone region to a level higher than
the top of Barronette Peak, but erosion since late Tertiary time has stripped the
volcanics from much of the Park area. The volcanic rocks (Eocene in age, fig. 5) rest
directly on Paleozoic sedimentary rocks along the line indicated. During the Laramide
orogeny, in Late Cretaceous and early Tertiary times, the region was folded and
uplifted into mountains. Thousands of feet of Mesozoic and Paleozoic sedimentary
rocks were then eroded off the rising mountains before the Absaroka volcanic rocks
were deposited. (Fig. 18)

GIANT PETRIFIED TREE TRUNKS in Yellowstone's fossil forest. The enclosing rocks, ▷
part of the Absaroka volcanic sequence that forms Specimen Ridge, are approximately
50 million years old. Many of the tree trunks are still upright, having been smothered
and buried in their original positions by breccia, ash, and dust from nearby volcanoes.
It is evident that more than one "forest" is represented in this view. Prof. Erling
Dorf, of Princeton University, counted a total of 27 different forest layers in the rocks
now exposed at Specimen Ridge. He also determined that the most common kinds of
trees were sycamore, walnut, magnolia, chestnut, oak, redwood, maple, and dogwood.
The nearest living relatives of many of these trees are now found in the warm-
temperate to subtropical forests of the southeastern and southern United States.
(National Park Service photograph.) (Fig. 19)

28

LCANIC   ROCKS

DIMENTARY   ROCKS

of Dunraven Pass several thin igneous dikes cut through volcanic breccias. These dikes radiate outward from the nearby central core of the volcano, which lies east of the highway in the vicinity of Washburn Hot Springs. From Dunraven Pass northward for 2 – 3 miles, the road is lined with lava flows and very coarse breccias that accumulated close to the volcanic neck (fig. 17). Farther north toward Tower Falls, breccias and conglomerates predominate, but the average size of individual rock fragments decreases gradually northward away from the center of eruption. Beds of sandstone then begin to appear in the sequence, having been deposited mainly by streams that drained the north slope of the volcano.

At the end of Absaroka volcanism, approximately 40 million years ago (fig. 6), all of Yellowstone lay buried beneath several thousand feet of lavas, breccias, and ash (fig. 18). The landscape must have appeared as a gently rolling

IGNEOUS ROCK. Closeup view of intrusive igneous rock (diorite) from the Electric Peak stock in the Gallatin Range; Electric Peak is pictured in figure 37. The rock is composed chiefly of light-colored quartz and feldspar and dark-colored iron and magnesium silicate minerals. (Fig. 20)

BUNSEN PEAK, a roughly circular body of intrusive igneous rock, is the eroded remnant of either the "neck" of an Absaroka volcano or a small stock that solidified directly beneath a volcano. The peak rises approximately 1,200 feet above a flat plain (foreground) that is covered by flows of younger basalt. The Yellowstone Tuff, formed by volcanic ash and dust exploded from the central Yellowstone region to the south, underlies the basalt. When erupted, the volcanic debris (as well as the basalt lava) flowed around this high-standing peak. (Fig. 21)

plateau, drained by sluggish, meandering streams and dotted here and there by volcanoes still rising above the general level of the ground. This plateau surface, however, probably stood at a maximum of only a few thousand feet above sea level, for animals and plants now found as fossils in the Absaroka volcanic rocks indicate that warm-temperature to even subtropical climates existed during the volcanic period (fig. 19).

A quiet period

Little is known in detail of the geologic events in Yellowstone during Oligocene and Miocene times. Rocks of these ages have not been recognized within the Park; if ever deposited there, they have since been removed by erosion or buried by younger volcanic rocks. Thus, we can only speculate as to what events took place during this 25-million-year period. No doubt the broad Absaroka volcanic plateau was eroded, but not deeply, because the topographic relief and stream gradients of the region remained low. There are also hints that some volcanic activity took place, for volcanic rocks representing parts of this time interval occur south of the Park, and some of these rocks may have originated within the Park area. Little transpired, however, to significantly alter the existing geological makeup of the Park; it was indeed a quiet time, particularly when compared with the extremely dynamic periods which immediately preceded and followed it.

More mountain building and deep erosion

Many features of the present-day landscape of Yellowstone stem from Pliocene time, about 10 million years ago. At that time the entire region — in fact, much of the Rocky Mountain chain — was being uplifted by giant earth movements to heights several thousand feet above its previous level. This episode of regional uplift accounts in large measure for the present high average elevation of the Yellowstone country. Although the precise cause of the uplift is unknown, the uplift assuredly reflects profound changes that were taking place deep within or beneath the earth's crust.

Great tensional forces, operating during Pliocene time, pulled the Yellowstone region apart and partially broke it into large steep-sided blocks bounded by *normal faults* (fig. 13). Some blocks sank while others rose, commonly on the order of several thousand feet. The Gallatin Range, in the northwest corner of the Park, for example, was lifted as a rectangular mountain block along north-trending 20-mile-long normal faults that border it on each side (fig. 14, section A–A′; pl. 1). In the south-central part of the Park, the differential movements between several adjacent fault blocks totaled more than 15,000 feet (fig. 14, section C–C′). Farther south, the Teton Range moved up and the floor of Jackson Hole moved down along a normal-fault zone that stretches along the east foot of the range. An enormous offset of about 30,000 feet developed between the two crustal blocks, accounting in large part for the now incredibly steep and rugged east face of the Teton Range.

The pronounced rise in elevation of the general ground surface and the chopping of the region into many mountainous fault blocks caused a profound increase in the rate of erosion. Once-sluggish streams turned into vigorous, fast-moving rivers that began to cut deeply into the Absaroka volcanic plateau. Huge quantities of rock debris were stripped off and carried out of the area, and at the end of the Pliocene, the Yellowstone region must have been very highly dissected mountains and table- and canyon-lands. Much of the landscape may have resembled the rugged terrain now seen in the Absaroka Range along the east side of the Park. These mountains (fig. 27), and the Washburn Range in the interior of the Park (fig. 4), today represent but small remnants of the vast pile of Absaroka volcanic rocks that once covered all of Yellowstone and the surrounding regions.

Formation of the Yellowstone Caldera

We have now approached that point in geologic time—
the beginning of the Quaternary Period between 2 million
and 3 million years ago—when the stage was set for the
triggering of those all-important events that culminated in
the development of the 1,000-square-mile Yellowstone caldera
and ultimately gave rise to the world-renowned hot-water and
steam phenomena. Involved were some of the earth's biggest
explosions, which have had no apparent counterpart in recorded human history. A few extremely explosive eruptions
have occurred historically, however, such as the one that took
place on the uninhabited island of Krakatoa, between Java
and Sumatra in the East Indies, during the latter part of
August 1883. For several days this island had been shaken by
a series of violent explosions. Then, on August 27, it was
ripped by an explosion that was heard as far away as Australia,
a distance of about 3,000 miles. Fifty-mile-high dust clouds
became windborne around the globe, producing colorful sun-
rises and sunsets in all parts of the world for several years.
When the air around Krakatoa finally cleared, it was found
that two-thirds of the island, some 12 square miles, had collapsed and vanished into the sea. Though the Krakatoa eruption resulted in a caldera that is only a small fraction of the
size of the one in Yellowstone, it provides a mental picture
to help us understand what has been discovered about the
great volcanic holocaust in Yellowstone National Park that
was described briefly in an early part of this report.

Near the beginning of the Quaternary Period a vast
quantity of molten rock had again accumulated deep within
the earth beneath Yellowstone. This time, in contrast to
Absaroka volcanism, the magma was charged with highly ex-

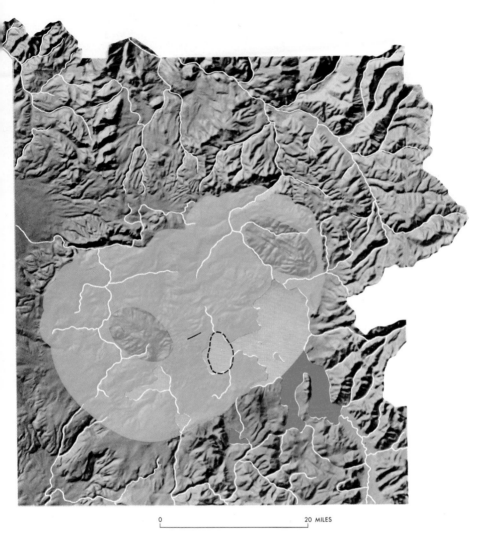

0 |_____| 20 MILES

OUTLINE OF THE YELLOWSTONE CALDERA produced by the enormous volcanic eruption 600,000 years ago. The two oval-shaped areas are resurgent domes that arched the caldera floor over twin magma chambers after the eruption. The margins of the resurgent domes are surrounded by ring fracture zones which extend outward toward the edge of the caldera. Numerous fractures in these zones provided escape routes through which lavas of the Plateau Rhyolite oozed to the surface and poured out across the caldera floor. Today these zones also provide underground channels for the circulation of hot water in the Yellowstone thermal system. The area outlined by the dotted line shows the smaller and younger inner caldera now occupied by the West Thumb of Yellowstone Lake. (Based on information supplied by R. L. Christiansen and H. R. Blank, Jr.; the existence of a caldera in Yellowstone National Park was first recognized by F. R. Boyd in the late 1950's.) (Fig. 22)

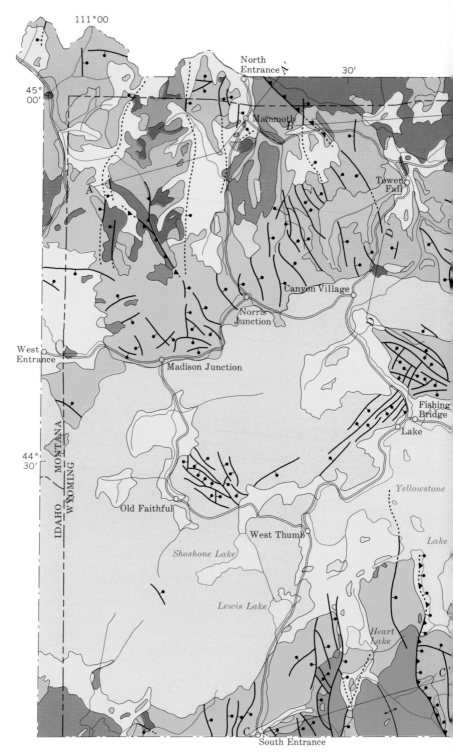

GEOLOGIC MAP OF YELLOWSTONE NATIONAL PAR

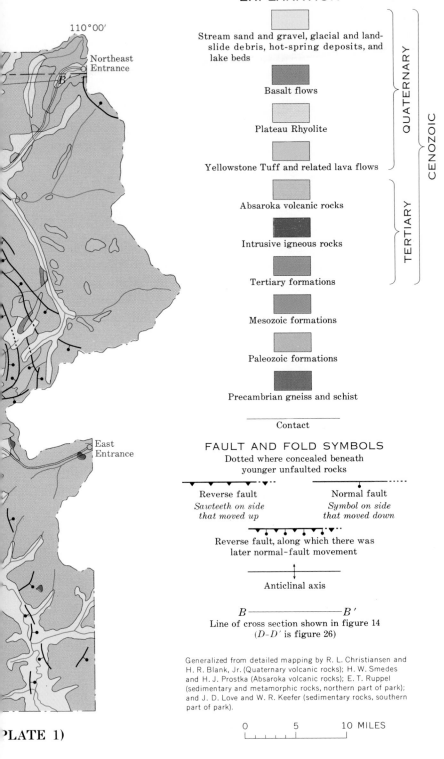

EXPLANATION

Stream sand and gravel, glacial and landslide debris, hot-spring deposits, and
lake beds

Basalt flows

Plateau Rhyolite

Yellowstone Tuff and related lava flows

Absaroka volcanic rocks

Intrusive igneous rocks

Tertiary formations

Mesozoic formations

Paleozoic formations

Precambrian gneiss and schist

———————

Contact

FAULT AND FOLD SYMBOLS

Dotted where concealed beneath
younger unfaulted rocks

Reverse fault
Sawteeth on side
that moved up

Normal fault
Symbol on side
that moved down

Reverse fault, along which there was
later normal-fault movement

Anticlinal axis

B ————————— B'
Line of cross section shown in figure 14
(*D-D'* is figure 26)

Generalized from detailed mapping by R. L. Christiansen and
H. R. Blank, Jr. (Quaternary volcanic rocks); H. W. Smedes
and H. J. Prostka (Absaroka volcanic rocks); E. T. Ruppel
(sedimentary and metamorphic rocks, northern part of park);
and J. D. Love and W. R. Keefer (sedimentary rocks, southern
part of park).

0   5   10 MILES

QUATERNARY

TERTIARY

CENOZOIC

110°00'

Northeast
Entrance

B

East
Entrance

PLATE 1)

plosive materials which eventually caused two caldera-making eruptions, one 2,000,000 years ago and the other 600,000 years ago. Because both eruptions affected the central part of the Park, the features related to the older one were largely destroyed by the activity associated with the younger one. Thus, the outline of the volcanic caldera we now see in the Yellowstone landscape is chiefly the one that formed 600,000 years ago (fig. 22). The sequence of events described in the following pages, and illustrated diagrammatically in figure 23, is based on studies of this later eruption; the pattern for the 2,000,000-year-old eruption probably was similar.

The eruption

The giant reservoir of molten rock that built up beneath the Park area fed two large magma chambers that rose to within a few thousand feet of the surface. As the pressures increased, the overlying ground arched, stretched, and cracked (fig. 23A). Small amounts of lava began to flow out through the cracks in places, but finally, in a great surge of rapid, violently explosive eruptions, first from one chamber and then the other, mountains of hot pumice, ash, and rock debris spewed from the earth (fig. 23B). The dense, swirling masses of erupted material spread out across the countryside in extremely fast moving *ash flows,* swept along by hot expanding gases trapped within them. Large quantities of ash and dust were also blown high into the air and dispersed by the wind. Thin layers of airborne volcanic ash from Yellowstone are now found throughout much of the central and western United States.

The ash flows (fig. 23B), as they sped across the Yellowstone countryside, first filled the old canyons and valleys that had been eroded into the Absaroka volcanic pile and older rocks during Pliocene time. Eventually much of this older landscape was buried by ash. Some of the larger highlands, such as Mount Washburn and adjacent ridges and Bunsen Peak, however, stood well above the level of the sweeping ash flows; so the debris flowed around them rather than across them (fig. 21). Finally coming to rest, the hot pumice, ash, and rock particles settled down in vast horizontal sheets (fig. 24). Upon cooling and crystallizing, the particles welded together to form a series of compact rocks with the composition of rhyolite (figs. 15 and 25). The term "ash-flow tuff" (also, the term "welded tuff") is commonly used to describe these rocks, which now make up the Yellowstone Tuff (fig. 5).

The collapse

With the sudden removal of hundreds of cubic miles of molten rock from underground, the roofs of the twin magma chambers collapsed. Enormous blocks of rock fell in above each of the chambers, and a great crater, or *caldera,* broke the ground surface in central Yellowstone (fig. 23C). The exact depth to which the original surface collapsed is unknown, but it must have been several thousand feet. The subsidence took place chiefly along large vertical, or normal, faults in the ring fracture zones above the margins of the magma chambers (fig. 22). Abundant, though less extensive, normal faults also formed outside the caldera proper, as the surrounding areas adjusted to the staggering impact of the explosive eruptions and subsequent collapse.

Because the Yellowstone caldera now lies partly buried by thick lava flows, the appearance of the caldera today is not nearly as impressive as it must have been when the caldera was first formed. Many of the important features, however, are particularly well exposed in the vicinity of Canyon Village (fig. 26). The steep south slope of the nearby Washburn Range (fig. 4) marks the north edge of the caldera, and the range itself stands high because it was not involved in the collapse. Canyon Village, on the other hand, lies at a much lower elevation within the caldera proper. Turnouts on the road just south of Dunraven Pass provide especially fine views of the northern part of the caldera, and on a clear day Flat Mountain and the Red Mountains, which mark the south edge of the caldera, south of Yellowstone Lake, can be seen 50 miles away. As might be expected, the large basin occupied by Yellowstone Lake owes its existence in part to caldera collapse. The south edge of the caldera cuts across the south-central part of the lake, along Flat Mountain Arm and the north tip of the Promontory; the east edge coincides approximately with the east edge of the lake north of Southeast Arm (fig. 27). Also, the prominent bluffs north of the Madison River near Madison Junction mark part of the north rim of the caldera.

39

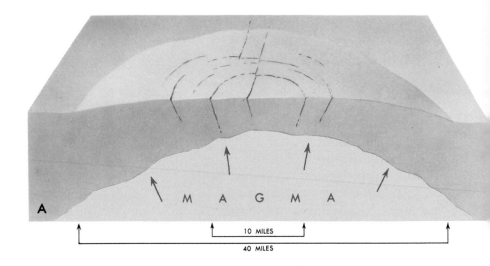

A

10 MILES

40 MILES

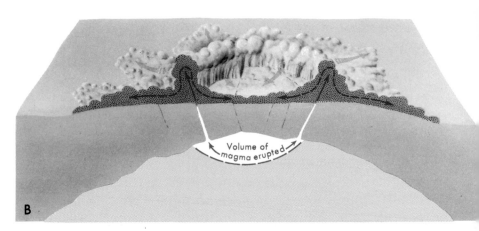

Volume of
magma erupted

B

CALDERA DEVELOPMENT. Schematic diagrams showing idealized stages in the development of the Yellowstone caldera 600,000 years ago. The scales shown in Diagram A
are approximately the size of the features in Yellowstone. Although only one magma
chamber is pictured in the diagrams, two chambers were involved in the Yellowstone
eruption. (Based on information supplied by R. L. Christiansen and H. R. Blank, Jr.)

A, A large magma chamber formed deep within the earth, and the molten rock began
to force its way slowly toward the surface. As it pushed upward, it arched the
overlying rocks into a broad dome. The arching produced a series of concentric
fractures, or a ring fracture zone, around the crest of the dome. The fractures
extended downward toward the top of the magma chamber.

B, The ring fractures eventually tapped the magma chamber, the uppermost part of
which contained a high proportion of dissolved gases. With the sudden release of

40

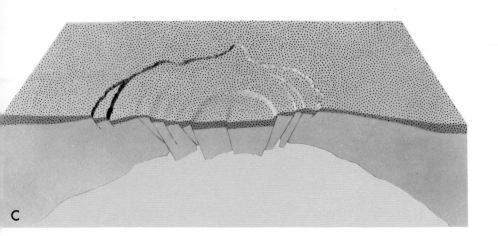

C

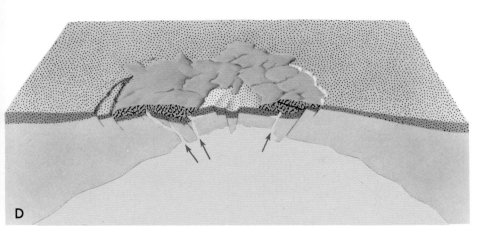

D

pressure, tremendous amounts of hot gases and molten rock were erupted almost instantly. The liquid solidified into pumice, ash, and dust as it was blown out. Some of the dust and ash was blown high into the air and carried along by the wind, but much of the debris moved outward across the landscape as vast ash flows, covering thousands of square miles very rapidly.

C, The area overlying the blown-out part of the magma chamber collapsed to form a gigantic caldera. The collapse took place mostly along normal faults that developed from the fractures in the ring fracture zone. The depth of the collapse was probably several thousand feet.

D, Renewed rise of molten rock domed the caldera floor above the magma chamber. A series of rhyolite lava flows poured out through fractures in the surrounding ring fracture zone and spread across the caldera floor. (Fig. 23)

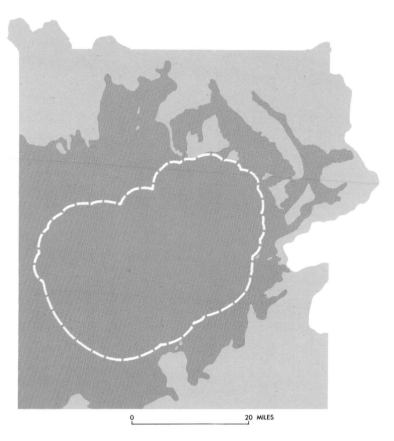

0   20 MILES

ORIGINAL EXTENT OF THE YELLOWSTONE TUFF (ash-flow tuff) that covered most of Yellowstone National Park about 600,000 years ago. The tuff was erupted explosively from the ring fracture zones of the Yellowstone caldera. The outline of the caldera is shown by the dashed line. (Based on information supplied by R. L. Christiansen and H. R. Blank, Jr.) (Fig. 24)

YELLOWSTONE TUFF AT GOLDEN GATE. The rocks consist of layered ash-flow tuff; the ▷ height of the cliff is about 200 feet. Closeup B shows typical characteristics of the tuff in most outcrop areas. Of the light-colored materials, the larger masses are compressed pumice fragments and the smaller masses are pumice, feldspar, and quartz. The dark grains are chiefly magnetite and pyroxene. Closeup A is of a coarse-grained specimen from Tuff Cliff. The large fragments are mostly crystallized pumice, and the light-colored matrix is composed of very fine particles of volcanic ash and dust. (Fig. 25)

42

├─1 INCH─┤

A   B

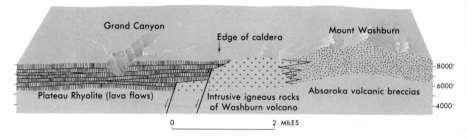

GEOLOGIC CROSS SECTION showing generalized relationships along the north edge of the Yellowstone caldera in the Mount Washburn – Canyon area (line of section labeled D–D' on pl. 1). The caldera subsided along normal faults in the ring fracture zone, and the Plateau Rhyolite (lava flows) poured out across the caldera floor between 600,000 and 500,000 years ago. The faults cut across the central intrusive igneous core of the 50-million-year-old (Eocene) Washburn volcano; the north half of the volcano is still preserved, but the south half subsided as part of the caldera and is now buried by lava flows. (Based on information supplied by H. J. Prostka and R. L. Christiansen.) (Fig. 26)

The outpouring of lava

The final violent eruption 600,000 years ago, although releasing much of the explosive energy of the gases contained in the magma, did not quell all potential volcanic activity in the twin chambers. Molten rock again rose in both of them, and in a few hundreds or thousands of years the overlying caldera floor was domed over the two chambers. One of these prominent domes lies near Old Faithful and the other east of Hayden Valley (figs. 22 and 23D). Soon, too, the magma found its way upward through the wide ring fracture zones encircling the caldera. Pouring out rather quietly from many openings (fig. 23D), the lavas flooded the caldera floor and began to fill the still-smoldering pit. The first lavas appeared soon after the collapse 600,000 years ago, and the latest ones only 60,000 – 75,000 years ago. The flows were confined chiefly to the caldera proper, but here and there they spilled out across the rim, particularly toward the southwestern part of the Park (fig. 28). Some flows also erupted along fractures

44

YELLOWSTONE LAKE. View southeast across Yellowstone Lake toward the western foothills and crest of the Absaroka Range. The Absaroka Range is an erosional remnant of a vast pile of volcanic lavas and breccias (Absaroka volcanic rocks) that once covered all of Yellowstone; the lake occupies part of the Yellowstone caldera. (Fig. 27)

outside the caldera, the most prominent flow being the very famous one at Obsidian Cliff (fig. 29).

The chief rock type in the lava flows is rhyolite, similar in composition to the welded tuffs erupted earlier but different in other major characteristics. The rock, for example, shows much contorted layering as evidence of having flowed as a thick liquid across the ground (fig. 30). A coarse brecciated texture is also a common feature, well shown by lavas along the Firehole Canyon drive (fig. 31). Locally, some parts of the flows cooled so rapidly that few crystals formed, and the lava solidified mainly into a natural glass (fig. 32).

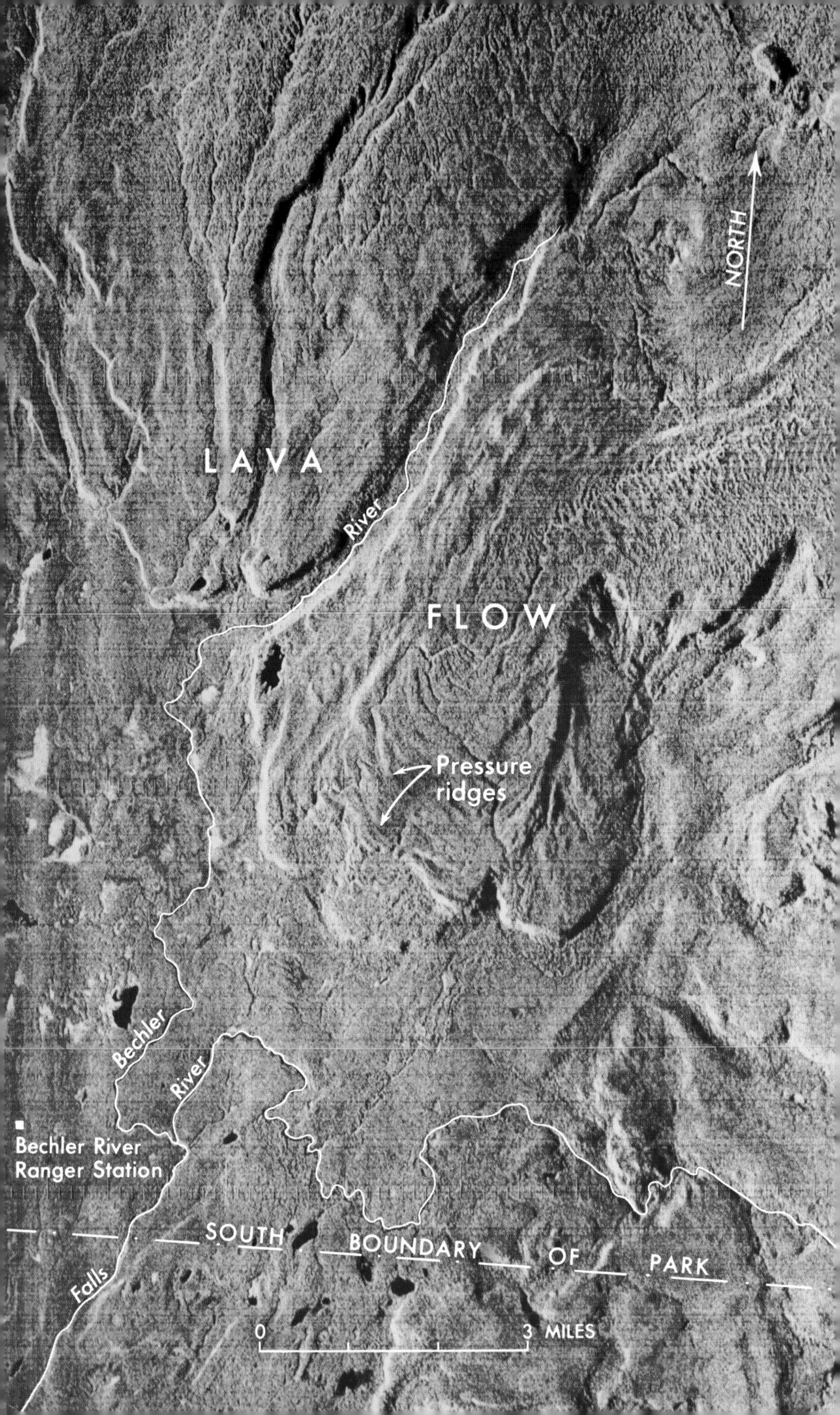

NORTH

LAVA

FLOW

River

Pressure
ridges

Bechler

River

■
Bechler River
Ranger Station

SOUTH BOUNDARY OF PARK

Falls

0   3 MILES

OBSIDIAN CLIFF, Jim Bridger's famous "mountain of glass." The rock is rhyolite lava which contains a high proportion of obsidian, a kind of black volcanic glass. Note columnar jointing along the sides of the cliff, similar to that shown by the basalt flows at Tower (fig. 33). The cliff is approximately 200 feet high. (Fig. 29)

◁ RADAR IMAGE of a part of southwestern Yellowstone National Park. The lobate land-forms are the edges of a lava flow of the Plateau Rhyolite that forms the Pitchstone Plateau (fig. 1). The low concentric ridges that parallel the toe of the flow are pressure ridges produced by the wrinkling of the nearly solidified crust of lava along the edge of the flow. (Image courtesy of National Aeronautics and Space Administration.) (Fig. 28)

47

⊢1 INCH⊣

THICK RHYOLITE LAVA FLOW along west bank of Firehole River. Closeup view is of a cut surface of rhyolite, showing the striking banding that results from the flowage of viscous molten rock. The dark bands are chiefly concentrations of volcanic glass (also some cavities), and the light bands are concentrations of tiny crystals of feldspar and quartz. (Fig. 30)

BRECCIATED RHYOLITE LAVA FLOWS along the Firehole Canyon drive. As a lava flow moves outward from its center of eruption, a chilled crust develops along its upper surface and outer edges because of the cooler temperatures in those parts of the flow. Continued movement of the still-molten rock in the interior of the flow causes this crust to break up (brecciate) into angular blocks. The blocks are then tumbled along until the whole mass finally solidifies. (Fig. 31)

49

A

B

OUTCROP OF GLASSY RHYOLITE LAVA along the road between Canyon Village and Norris Junction. The conspicuous lines in the face of the rock outline different layers produced by lava flowage. In closeup A, dark parts of the rock are volcanic glass (closeup B shows glassy fracture) and light-colored crystals are quartz (blocky) and feldspar (tabular). The feldspar crystals are alined parallel to the direction of flow. (Fig. 32)

About 30 different flows have been recognized. Grouped within a major rock unit called the Plateau Rhyolite (fig. 5), they cover more than 1,000 square miles. The gently rolling plateau surface of central Yellowstone, broken here and there by clusters of low-lying hills and ridges, is essentially the landscape that characterized the upper surfaces of the lava flows soon after they cooled and solidified. Natural valleys formed between some of the adjacent flows, and in places streams still follow these readymade channels. Rhyolite, in both lava flows and ash-flow tuffs, is by far the predominant rock type seen along the Park roads.

Several basalt flows were erupted along with the more common rhyolite flows, and in the vicinity of Tower Falls they form some of the most unusual rock units in the whole Park area (fig. 33). As the flows cooled, contraction cracks broke the basalt into a series of upright many-sided columns; from a distance they appear as a solid row of fenceposts. They are now covered by younger rocks, but if one could see the upper flat surface of the basalt layers where just the ends of the columns are sticking out, the pattern would be like that seen in a honeycomb.

During the eruptions of the Plateau Rhyolite, at least one relatively small caldera-making event occurred in the central Yellowstone region. This "inner" caldera developed sometime between 125,000 and 200,000 years ago, forming the deep depression now filled by the West Thumb of Yellowstone Lake (fig. 22). Like the main Yellowstone caldera, but on a much smaller scale, it formed as a direct result of the explosive eruption of rhyolitic ash flows and subsequent collapse of an oval-shaped area approximately 4 miles wide and 6 miles long. West Thumb is nearly the same size as Crater Lake, Oregon, which occupies one of the world's best-known calderas.

With the outpouring of the last lava flows 60,000 – 75,000 years ago, the forces of Quaternary volcanism finally died down. The hot-water and steam activity, however, still remains as a vivid reminder of Yellowstone's volcanic past. But who can say even now that we are witnessing the final stage of volcanism? Someday, quite conceivably, there might be yet another outburst of molten rock — only time, of course, will tell.

├─ 1 INCH ─┤

Final Sculpturing of the Landscape

The many episodes of mountain building and volcanism all left their lasting and unmistakable imprints across the face of the Yellowstone country. During the latter part of the Tertiary Period, erosion, too, had begun to make its own deep marks. But only in the last 100,000 years or so have the powerful exterior forces of the earth — chiefly running water and moving ice — had a virtually free hand in shaping the Park's landscape. Nevertheless, in this short period of time they have wrought profound changes.

Glaciation

A giant boulder of Precambrian gneiss lies among the trees beside the road leading to Inspiration Point on the north rim of the Grand Canyon of the Yellowstone (fig. 34). This boulder, measuring approximately 24×20×18 feet and weighing at least 500 tons, is of considerable interest, not so much for its great size but because it is completely out-of-place in its present surroundings. The boulder rests on rhyolite lava flows of Quaternary age, at least 15 miles from the nearest outcrops of the ancient gneiss to the north and northeast. Obviously, this seemingly immovable chunk of

◁ TWO LEDGES OF BASALT spectacularly exposed in the east wall of the Grand Canyon of the Yellowstone at The Narrows near Tower Falls. Pronounced columnar jointing of the basalt is seen at close range (bottom photograph) at the edge of the road on the opposite (west) side of the canyon. Inset shows the dense character of the black basalt, which consists of microscopic crystals of feldspar, pyroxene, olivine, and magnetite. The light-colored rocks between the basalt flows (top photograph) are ancient stream gravels deposited about 1½ million years ago, when the channel of the Yellowstone River was farther east and not as deep as it is today. The hill is capped by lake sediments, sand, and gravel deposited when the Yellowstone River was blocked by a glacial dam farther downstream (to the left). The brown rocks at the base of the cliff are Absaroka andesite breccias. (Fig. 33)

53

rock was pushed or carried a long way by some very powerful transporting agent before it was finally dropped. A natural force of such magnitude could only have been exerted by moving ice; in fact, no further proof than this one boulder is needed for us to conclude beyond question that glaciers once existed in Yellowstone. There is, to be sure, much additional evidence that the Park region was extensively glaciated. Deposits of out-of-place boulders (*glacial erratics*), like the one mentioned above, are found nearly everywhere (fig. 35), and the mountains and high valleys still bear the vivid scars of ice sculpturing (figs. 36 and 37).

The principal requirement for the formation of glaciers is simple: more snow has to accumulate during the winter than is melted during the summer. If this condition continues for a long enough period of time (measured in centuries), the snow compacts to ice, and extensive icefields grow until they finally begin to move under their own weight, thereby becoming glaciers. Records show that the average year-round temperature is 32°–33°F along Yellowstone Lake, 35°F at Old Faithful, and 39°F at Mammoth. Each winter, snow accumulates to depths of 5–10 feet throughout much of the Park. If the average annual temperatures were to decrease a few degrees or the yearly snowfall were to increase a foot or so, either change could possibly herald the beginning of another ice age in the Yellowstone region.

Yellowstone was glaciated at least three times. These glaciations are, from oldest to youngest, the pre-Bull Lake, Bull Lake, and Pinedale. Their precise age and duration are imperfectly known, but estimates based on a few radiometric determinations are: (1) the oldest glaciation (pre-Bull Lake glaciation) began more than 300,000 years ago and ended between 180,000 and 200,000 years ago; (2) Bull Lake Glaciation began about 125,000 years ago and ended more than 45,000 years ago; (3) Pinedale Glaciation began about 25,000 years ago and ended about 8,500 years ago. The pre-Bull Lake and Bull Lake are known only from scattered deposits of rock debris (*glacial moraines*) and other features, but the distribution of these deposits indicates that glaciers were widespread throughout the region and occurred both between and during eruptions of the Plateau Rhyolite. The effects of the Pinedale glaciers, on the other hand, are obvious in many parts of the Park, and the history of this youngest glacial cycle (described below) is known in much greater detail than that of the two older ones.

In the early stages of Pinedale Glaciation, an enormous icefield built up in the high Absaroka Range southeast of the Park area. A glacier, fed by this icefield, flowed northward

◁ GIANT BOULDER (glacial erratic) of Precambrian gneiss near Inspiration Point on the north rim of the Grand Canyon. The boulder, measuring 24×20×18 feet and weighing more than 500 tons, was dropped at this locality by glacial ice; it now rests on the much younger Plateau Rhyolite. The distance that the boulder was carried or pushed was at least 15 miles. (Fig. 34)

GLACIATED TERRAIN along the Northeast Entrance road. The boulders, many of them measuring 10 feet across or more, were carried into the area by ice flowing down Slough Creek from mountains north of the Park during the Pinedale Glaciation. As the glaciers melted, the boulders were left stranded in hummocky, morainal deposits. Shallow depressions in the irregular topography are now commonly filled by small ponds. (Fig. 35)

down the upper Yellowstone valley and into the basin now occupied by Yellowstone Lake. At about the same time, another great icefield formed in the mountains north of the Park and sent long tongues of ice southward toward the lower Yellowstone and Lamar River valleys. Smaller valley glaciers flowed westward out of the Absaroka Range along the east edge of the Park, and still others formed along the main ridges and valleys of the Gallatin Range, in the northwestern part of the Park. Thus, many huge masses of ice from the north, east, and southeast converged and met in the Park.

For the next 10,000 years, the ice thickened and spread out over more and more of the Park area. The mass centered over the Yellowstone Lake basin grew to a depth of 3,000 feet or more and dominated the entire scene; it formed a broad "mountain" of ice which became so high that it caused more snow to fall upon itself and was cold enough to prevent much of this snow from melting. Eventually the Pinedale glaciers covered about 90 percent of Yellowstone (fig. 38).

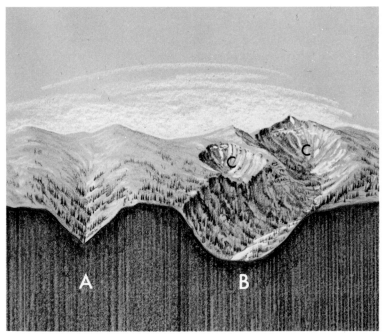

CANYON PROFILES. Typical profiles of a canyon cut by a stream (A) and of a canyon gouged by a glacier (B). Glacial cirques (C) are shown at the head and high on the side of the glaciated valley. (Fig. 36)

GLACIAL CIRQUE on east face of Electric Peak, northern Gallatin Range. During several episodes of glaciation, this steep-walled amphitheaterlike valley was cut and filled by ice which fed glaciers moving downslope to the lower right. The cirque floor is now covered by a thick deposit of rock rubble underlain in part by ice, and the whole mass is still moving slowly downhill as a rock glacier. The dark rock at lower right is part of the Electric Peak stock, composed of diorite (fig. 20) and other kinds of intrusive igneous rocks. The rocks in the cirque walls are chiefly Cretaceous shales (light to moderately dark color) with thin sills of igneous rock (very dark color). (West-looking oblique aerial photograph, courtesy of William B. Hall, University of Idaho.) (Fig. 37)

At this stage, probably about 15,000 years ago, only the west edge of the Park, and perhaps a few of the highest peaks and ridges within the Park, remained free of ice. It is interesting to note that although ice moved across and buried the ancestral Grand Canyon of the Yellowstone, it did not flow down and scour the canyon (fig. 36). If it had, the canyon would look much different than it does today (fig. 41).

After their maximum advance, the Pinedale glaciers began to melt, leaving behind the rock debris they had gouged from the landscape and had pushed or carried along with them. These glacial moraines are now found in many areas throughout the Park. In places, glacial ice and (or) rock debris formed natural dams across stream valleys, thereby impounding lakes. Parts of Hayden Valley, for example, contain layers of very fine sand, silt, and clay several tens of feet thick (fig. 39) that accumulated along the bottom of a large lake. This lake formed behind a glacial dam across the Yellowstone River near Upper Falls. Some of the glacial dams broke and released water catastrophically, causing giant floods; the occurrence of one such flood is particularly evident along the Yellowstone River valley near Gardiner, Montana.

By about 12,000 years ago the thick Pinedale ice sheet had melted entirely from the Yellowstone Lake basin and most other areas of the Park, although valley glaciers continued to exist in the mountains until about 8,500 years ago. Then, following a short period of total disappearance, small icefields formed again in the heads of some of the higher mountain valleys. Since the melting of the Pinedale ice, however, none has descended as a glacier into the lower stretches of the valleys. Even though a few snowfields persist locally throughout the summers (except during the warmest years), no glaciers exist in the Park at the present time.

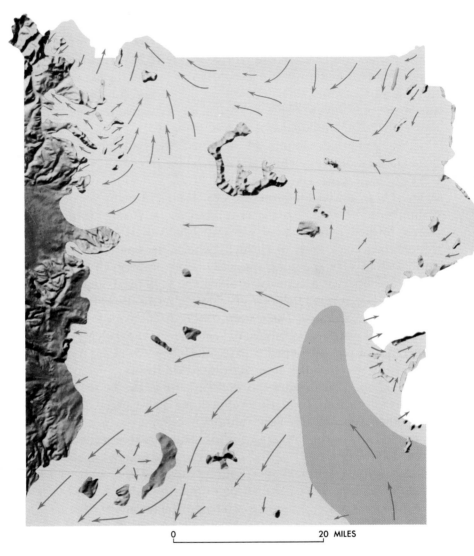

0   20 MILES

EXTENT OF ICE in Yellowstone National Park during the maximum spreading of the Pinedale glaciers, probably about 15,000 years ago. Long arrows indicate direction of strong flowage of ice; short arrows show direction of less vigorous ice flowage. The dark-blue area shows the main ice mass centered over the Yellowstone Lake basin in the southeast corner of the Park. Many of the high peaks and ridges such as Mount Washburn, which are here shown free of ice, were glaciated at least once during the past 250,000 years. Whether they were covered by the Pinedale glaciers, however, is still an unresolved question. (Based on information supplied by G. M. Richmond, K. L. Pierce, and H. A. Waldrop.) (Fig. 38)

FLAT-LYING BEDS of fine sand, silt, and clay near the mouth of Trout Creek in Hayden Valley. These beds were deposited in a glacially dammed lake that covered part of Hayden Valley when the Pinedale glaciers were melting. The height of the streambank is about 40 feet. (Fig. 39)

Running water—canyons and waterfalls

Yellowstone is, among its many attributes, the source of large and mighty rivers. Located across the Continental Divide, the Park feeds two of the most extensive drainage systems in the nation — (1) the Missouri River system (and ultimately the Mississippi River) on the Atlantic side, via the Yellowstone, Madison, and Gallatin Rivers, and (2) the Columbia River system on the Pacific side, via the Snake River (fig. 1). These streams are fed by an annual precipitation which averages about 17 inches at Old Faithful and Mammoth, but which is considerably greater in the mountain ranges.

Many stretches of the main river valleys in Yellowstone are broad and flat bottomed. In these, the stream gradients range from about 10 to 30 feet per mile, and there is little erosion going on at present (Hayden Valley is a good example, fig. 4). But here and there the gradients are steeper, and the valleys are narrow and rugged. In some places these streams drop 50 or even 100 feet per mile, and the fast-moving waters have carved deep V-shaped gorges (fig. 36).

Waterfalls, features for which Yellowstone is also justly famous (fig. 40), generally result from abrupt differences in rock hardness. If a stream flows over rocks that are more resistant to erosion than the rocks immediately downstream, a ledge or bench will form across the streambed at that place

◁ WATERFALLS in Yellowstone National Park.

A, Lewis Falls on the Lewis River. The falls cascade over the steep edge of a rhyolite lava flow.

B, Upper Falls on the Yellowstone River. The brink of the falls marks the contact between dense, resistant rhyolite lava (which forms the massive cliff) and more easily eroded rhyolite lava containing a high proportion of volcanic glass immediately downstream, as shown in figure 42.

C, Gibbon Falls on the Gibbon River. The river tumbles over a scarp etched in the Yellowstone Tuff. The scarp first formed along faults at the north edge of the Yellowstone caldera 600,000 years ago, at a point that now lies ¼ to ½ mile downstream. Continued erosion has caused the falls to recede northward to their present position.

D, Tower Falls on Tower Creek. The rocks at the brink of the falls, and in the vertical cliff beneath, are coarse breccias and conglomerates of the Absaroka volcanic rocks. The channel of Tower Creek has not been cut down rapidly enough to keep pace with the downcutting of the main channel of the Yellowstone River, which lies a short distance downstream from the base of the falls. (Fig. 40)

63

because the less resistant rocks are worn away faster. And, as the ledge becomes higher, the softer downstream rocks will erode even faster. A true waterfall is one in which there is a free, vertical fall of water. If the ledge or ledges form only a rough, steep runway in the streambed, then the term "rapids" or "cascades" is more appropriate.

The existence of many waterfalls in Yellowstone today is due in large part to the fact that, because of recent volcanism and glaciation, much of the region's topography is very young in terms of geologic time. Streams, even some of the largest ones, have not had enough time to wear away all the features that may produce waterfalls, cascades, or rapids along their channels. This is particularly true along the margins of lava flows, where there are sharp dropoffs between the tops of the flows and the lower ground beyond. The Grand Canyon of the Yellowstone and the Upper and Lower Falls, well illustrate the erosive power of running water.

Grand Canyon of the Yellowstone

Except for Old Faithful, the Grand Canyon of the Yellowstone is probably the best known and most talked about and photographed feature in the Park (fig. 41). Although not so deep or wide as some of the other great canyons in America, its sheer ruggedness and beauty are breathtaking. Here the aptness of the name "Yellowstone" can be fully appreciated and understood, for the viewer is at once engulfed in a sea of yellow hues streaked and tinted with various shades of red and brown.

At first glance, the canyon may appear to be a giant crack which suddenly opened up and into which the Yellowstone River then plunged headlong over high waterfalls at its southwest end. This, of course, is not the way the canyon formed. Nevertheless, it is apparent that certain unusual conditions caused the river, after winding slowly through flat-floored Hayden Valley for about 13 miles, to cut a precipitous gorge

GRAND CANYON AND LOWER FALLS of the Yellowstone River, as viewed upstream ▷ (southwest) from Artists Point on the south rim. The yellow-hued rocks lining the canyon walls are soft, hydrothermally altered rhyolite lavas. The rocks at the brink of the falls consist of less altered and therefore more resistant rhyolites. The falls, 309 feet high, formed at the contact between the hard and soft rhyolite units. (Photograph courtesy of Sgt. James E. Jensen, U.S. Air Force.) (Fig. 41)

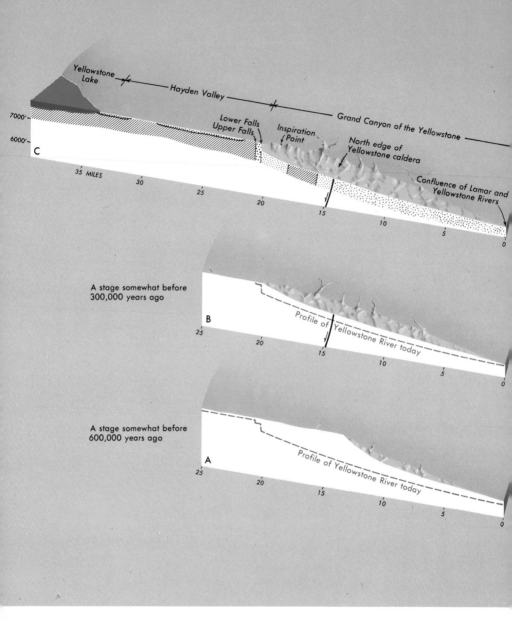

DEVELOPMENT OF GRAND CANYON. Profiles along the floor of the Grand Canyon of the Yellowstone as it appears today (C) and as it appeared at two older stages in its development (A and B). Note particularly the various kinds of rocks through which the canyon has been cut, and how rock differences have influenced the location of the two falls. Diagonal lines indicate unaltered rhyolite; large dots, rhyolite with much volcanic glass; small dots, hydrothermally altered rhyolite; and circles and dots, Absaroka volcanic rocks. (Based on information furnished by R. L. Christiansen and G. M. Richmond; vertical scale is exaggerated about 10 times.) (Fig. 42)

66

1,000 – 1,500 feet deep and 20 miles long (fig. 42C). A full explanation must be based on all the many events surrounding the eruption of the Yellowstone Tuff, the collapse of the Yellowstone caldera, the outpouring of the Plateau Rhyolite, and the various episodes of glaciation. Geologic studies show that all these events took place while the canyon was being cut, and that each one played an important role in its development. Hot-water and steam activity likewise was a significant factor. However, despite its many complexities, the history of the Grand Canyon can be divided into a few major stages, as outlined below:

1. From more than 2,000,000 years ago to about 600,000 years ago, a shallow canyon was gradually being cut into the Absaroka volcanic sequence by the ancestral Yellowstone River as it eroded headward from a point near the present confluence of the Yellowstone and Lamar Rivers (fig. 33). By the time of the climactic volcanic eruption in central Yellowstone 600,000 years ago, the head of the "old" canyon probably had been eroded southward nearly to the place where the north rim of the Yellowstone caldera was to form later (fig. 42A). This point now lies about 5 miles below Lower Falls.

2. Ash-flow tuffs that were erupted 600,000 years ago filled the "old" canyon, and the river recarved its channel, chiefly along its previous course.

3. A large lake formed behind (south of) the north rim of the caldera, the damming resulting in part from lava flows of Plateau Rhyolite that poured out across the caldera floor in this area between 600,000 and 500,000 years ago. Eventually the lake rose and spilled northward into the head of the "old" canyon, causing additional downcutting in what is now the lower 15-mile stretch of the canyon.

4. As the lake emptied, the river began to erode upstream into the thick rhyolite lava flows toward the present site of Lower Falls; the process was very similar to that of a common stream gully eroding headward into a hillside. At a stage somewhat more than 300,000 years ago, the head of the canyon probably lay near the falls, and the river had cut a channel 400 – 600 feet deep along this upper 5-mile stretch (fig. 42B).

5. Approximately 300,000 years ago the canyon area was covered by ice during pre-Bull Lake glaciation. During and after the retreat of this ice, sediments accumulated in a lake that occupied the upper reaches of the canyon between the present site of Upper Falls and Inspiration Point. Subsequently, very little downcutting was accomplished until about 150,000 – 125,000 years ago, when the canyon was eroded nearly to its present depth.

6. Canyon development was further interrupted by the advance and retreat of glaciers during Bull Lake and Pinedale Glaciations. During and since the melting of the Pinedale glaciers about 12,000 years ago, the canyon has attained its present depth, and its walls have acquired much of their picturesque erosional form. The Yellowstone River now maintains a fairly uniform gradient (60 – 80 feet per mile) throughout the 20-mile-long gorge, even though different segments of the canyon were cut at different times and through different kinds of rocks (fig. 42C).

The spectacular erosional development in the upper 5-mile segment of the Grand Canyon, which is the only part seen by most Park visitors, except for the very lower end near Tower Falls (fig. 33), has taken place mostly within the past 150,000 – 125,000 years. One reason for such a rapid rate of erosion stems from the fact that this part of the canyon overlies one of the wide ring fracture zones of the Yellowstone caldera (fig. 22). The fracture zone extends to great depth, providing a ready avenue of travel for the upflow of hot water and steam rising in the Yellowstone thermal system, as described in the following chapter. Through many thousands of years, the upward percolation of the hot fluids has caused severe chemical and physical changes (known as *hydrothermal alteration*) in the rhyolite lava flows. One spectacular result of the alteration has been the change from the normal brown and gray color of the rhyolites to the bright yellow and other colorful hues now seen in the canyon walls (as well as in many other places throughout the Park). Another significant result of alteration has been the weakening of the rocks; that is, the altered rocks are softer and less resistant to erosion than unaltered rocks. Hence, the river has been

68

able to erode these softer rocks, upstream to Lower Falls, at a very rapid rate.

The position of Lower Falls, as might be expected, coincides with a change from highly altered to less altered rhyolite; the difference in the erosion rates of the two kinds of rocks here is self-evident (figs. 41 and 42C). The position of Upper Falls is likewise closely controlled by differences in rock hardnesses. The rhyolites on the upstream side are hard and dense, whereas those on the downstream side contain a high proportion of volcanic glass which causes them to be more easily eroded (fig. 42C).

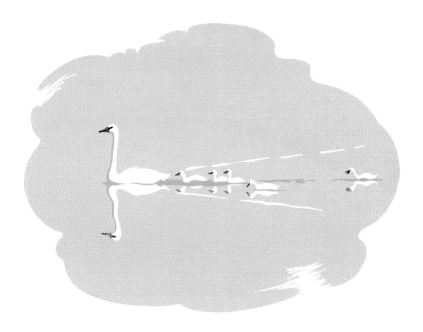

COMMON KINDS OF THERMAL FEATURES in Yellowstone National Park. A, Hot springs and terraces colored by algae at Mammoth Hot Springs; B, Castle Geyser erupting in Upper Geyser Basin; C, Fountain Paint Pots in Lower Geyser Basin; D, pool in Lower Geyser Basin. (Fig. 43)

70

Hot-Water and Steam Phenomena

Although Yellowstone is geologically outstanding in many ways, the great abundance, diversity, and spectacular nature of its thermal (hot-water and steam) features were undoubtedly the primary reasons for its being set aside as our first National Park (fig. 43). The unusual concentration of geysers, hot springs, mudpots, and fumaroles provides that special drawing card which has, for the past century, made the Park one of the world's foremost natural attractions.

To count all the individual thermal features in Yellowstone would be virtually impossible. Various estimates range from 2,500 to 10,000, depending on how many of the smaller features are included. They are scattered through many regions of the Park, but most are clustered in a few areas called geyser basins, where there are continuous displays of intense thermal activity. (See frontispiece.) The "steam" that can be seen in thermal areas is actually fog or water droplets condensed from steam; so the appearance of individual geyser basins depends largely on air temperature and humidity. On a warm, dry summer day, for example, the activity may seem very weak (fig. 44), except where individual geysers are erupting. On cold or very humid days, however, "steam" plumes are seen rising from every quarter.

How a thermal system operates

An essential ingredient for thermal activity is heat. A body of buried molten rock, such as the one that produced volcanic eruptions in Yellowstone as late as 60,000 to 75,000 years ago, takes a long time to cool. During cooling, tremendous quantities of heat are transmitted by conduction into the solid rocks surrounding the magma chamber (fig. 45).

NORRIS GEYSER BASIN, as viewed northward from the Norris Museum. This is one of the most active thermal areas in Yellowstone, but the photograph was taken on a warm dry summer day when little hot-water and steam activity was visible from a distance. Clouds of water droplets (the visible "steam" in thermal areas) normally form only when the air is cool and (or) moist. The floor of the basin is covered by a nearly solid layer of hot-spring deposits. (Fig. 44)

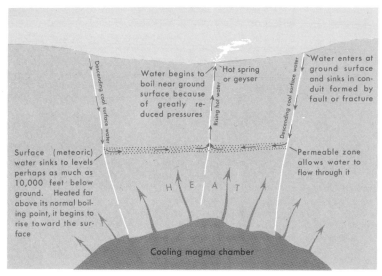

HEAT FLOW AND SURFACE WATER. Diagram showing a thermal system, according to the explanation that water of surface origin circulates and is heated at great depths. (Based on information supplied by D. E. White, L. J. P. Muffler, R. O. Fournier, and A. H. Truesdell.) (Fig. 45)

72

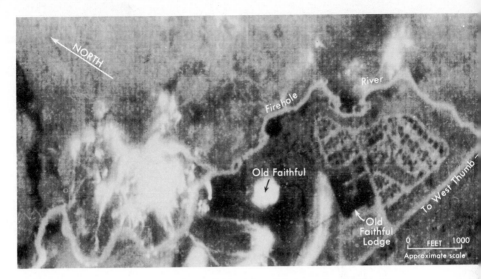

INFRARED IMAGE of a part of Upper Geyser Basin. Infrared instruments, sensitive to heat, are able to detect "hot" spots in the landscape. Note especially the sharp "image" of Old Faithful. (Image courtesy of National Aeronautics and Space Administration.) (Fig 46)

Eventually the whole region becomes much hotter than non-volcanic areas (fig. 46) . Normally, rock temperatures increase about 1°F per 100 feet of depth in the earth's crust, but in the thermally active areas of Yellowstone the rate of temperature increase is much greater. The amount of heat given off by the Upper Geyser Basin, for example, is 800 times the amount given off by normal (nonthermal) areas of the same size. This excess heat is enough to melt 1½ tons of ice per second! And, contrary to popular opinion, the underground temperatures have not cooled measurably in the 100 years that records have been kept on the thermal activity in the Park. In fact, geologic studies indicate that very high heat flows have continued for at least the past 40,000 years.

A second, equally essential ingredient for thermal activity is water. Many thousands of gallons are discharged by the hot springs and geysers in Yellowstone every minute — where does all this water come from? Studies show that nearly all the water originates above ground as rain or snow (meteoric water; fig. 45), and that very little comes from the underlying magma (magmatic water) .

The mechanism for heating the water, on the other hand, is a matter of some uncertainty. Until a few years ago the

73

heating was assumed to occur near the ground surface and to be caused by hot magmatic gases (mostly steam) rising from the underlying magma chamber. Deep wells drilled recently in many thermal areas throughout the world (including research drill holes in Yellowstone), however, suggest a better explanation. According to this explanation, the surface water enters underground passages (fractures and faults) and circulates to great depths — as much as 5,000 – 10,000 feet in some areas (fig. 45) — there to become heated far above its surface boiling point. Research drill holes in Yellowstone, for example, have demonstrated that water of surface origin exists at all depths at least to the maximum drilled (1,088 feet), and that the water reaches temperatures up to at least 465°F. The increase in temperature with depth causes a corresponding decrease in the weight (density) of the water. Because of this, the hot, "lighter," water begins to rise again toward the ground surface, pushed upward by the colder, "heavier," near-surface water which sinks to keep the water channels filled. Thus is set into motion a giant *convection current* which operates continuously to supply very hot water to the thermal areas (fig. 45). Just how deep the waters circulate in Yellowstone no one really knows; as a guess, the depth probably is at least 1 or 2 miles.

The effect of pressure on the boiling temperature of water also plays a vital role in thermal activity. In a body of water, the pressure at the surface is that exerted by the weight of air above it (*atmospheric pressure*). Water under these conditions boils at 212°F at sea level and at about 199°F at the elevation of most of the geyser basins in Yellowstone. However, water at depth not only is subjected to atmospheric pressure but also bears the added weight of the overlying water. Under such additional pressures, water boils only when the temperature is raised above its surface boiling point. In a well 100 feet deep at sea level, for example, the water at the bottom would have to be heated to 288°F before it will boil. Thus it follows that in the underground "workings" of hot springs or geysers, (1) The deepest water is subjected to the greatest pressures, and (2) these deeper waters (in Yellowstone) must be heated well above 199°F before they can actually begin to boil. By this same reasoning but in reverse, if the pressure is released, which happens as the water rises toward the ground surface, the "hotter-than-boiling" water will then begin to boil. The boiling will be rather quiet if the pressure is released gradually, as in most hot springs. But if the pressure is released suddenly, boiling may become so violent that much of the water flashes explosively into steam, expanding to several hundred times its normal volume. This expansion provides the necessary energy for geyser eruptions.

Hot-spring deposits and algae

Nearly all geysers and many hot springs build mounds or terraces of mineral deposits; some are so unusual in form that descriptive names have been given to them, such as Castle Geyser (fig. 47). These deposits are generally made

MOUND OF SINTER at Castle Geyser, Upper Geyser Basin. Lower part of mound has well-defined layers probably deposited by normal hot springs. The upper, irregular part resulted from the vigorous eruptions characteristic of geysers and marks a change in the local hot-spring activity. (Fig. 47)

├─1 INCH─┤

up of many very thin layers of rock. Each layer represents a crust or film of rock-forming mineral which was originally dissolved in hot water as it flowed through the underground rocks, and which was then precipitated as the water spread out over the surrounding ground surface.

In all major thermal areas of the Park, with the exception of Mammoth Hot Springs, most of the material being deposited is *sinter* (the kind found around geysers is popularly called *geyserite*). Its chief constituent is silica (the same as in quartz and in ordinary window glass). At Mammoth, the deposit is *travertine* (fig. 48), which consists almost entirely of calcium carbonate. The material deposited at any given place commonly reflects the predominant kind of rock through which the hot water has passed during its underground travels. At Mammoth Hot Springs the water passes through thick beds of limestone (which is calcium carbonate), but in other areas the main rock type through which the water percolates is rhyolite, a rock rich in silica.

Through centuries of intense activity, layers of sinter have built up on the floors of the geyser basins (fig. 44); these deposits are generally less than 10 feet thick. In one drill hole at Mammoth, deposits of travertine extend to a depth of 250 feet. Dead trees and other kinds of vegetation whose life processes have been choked off by the heat, water, and precipitated minerals of hot-spring activity are a common sight in many places (fig. 51).

Both travertine and sinter are white to gray. Around active hot springs, however, the terraces that are constantly under water may be brightly colored (figs. 43 and 49) because they are coated by microscopic plants called *algae*. These organisms, which thrive in hot water at temperatures up to about 170°F, are green, yellow, and brown. Oxides of iron and manganese also contribute to the coloring in some parts of the thermal areas. The delicate blue color of many pools, however, results from the reflection of light off the pool walls and back through the deep clear water (fig. 43). Other pools are yellow because they contain sulfur, or are green from the combined influence of yellow sulfur and "blue" water.

◁ TERRACES OF TRAVERTINE at Opal Springs, Mammoth Hot Springs area. Closeup view shows layered and porous nature of the travertine. (Fig. 48)

ALGAL-COLORED TERRACES lining the west bank of the Firehole River at Midway Geyser Basin. Algae are microscopic plants that grow profusely on rocks covered by hot water at temperatures up to about 170°F. (Fig. 49)

Hot springs and geysers

Hot springs occur where the rising hot waters of a thermal system issue from the ground-level openings of the feeder conduits (fig. 45). By far the greatest numbers discharge water and steam in a relatively steady noneruptive manner, although they vary considerably in individual behavior. Depending upon pressure, water temperature, rate of upflow, heat supply, and arrangement and size of underground passages, some hot springs boil violently and emit dense clouds of vapor whereas in others the water quietly wells up with little agitation from escaping steam. In some hot springs, however, the underground channels are too narrow or the upflow of very hot water and steam is too great to permit a steady discharge; periodic eruptions then result. These special kinds of springs are called "geysers" (from the Icelandic word *geysir,* meaning to "gush" or "rage"). At least 200 geysers, of which about 60 play to a height of 10 feet or more, occur in Yellowstone National Park; this is more than in any other region of the world.

How does a geyser work? We cannot, of course, observe the inner plumbing of a geyser, except for that part which is seen by looking into its uppermost "well." Deeper levels directly below the "well" can be probed by scientific instruments to some extent, and research drilling in some parts of the geyser basins also provides much useful information. The available information suggests that the plumbing system of a geyser (1) lies close to the ground surface, generally no deeper than a few hundred feet; (2) consists of a tube, commonly nearly vertical, that connects to chambers, side channels, or layers of porous rock, where substantial amounts of water can be stored; and (3) connects downward through the central tube and side channels to narrow conduits that rise from the deepwater source of the main thermal system.

Considering a geyser system as described above and applying what is known about the behavior of water and steam, we can understand what causes a natural thermal eruption. Figure 50 shows diagrammatically the succession of events believed to occur during the typical eruptive cycle of a geyser such as Old Faithful.

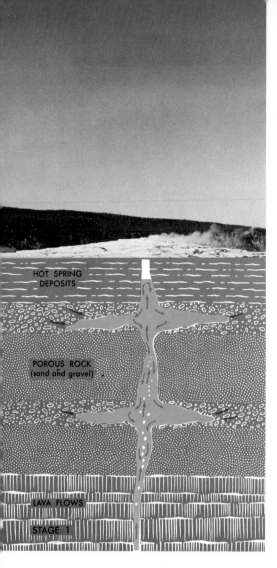

HOT SPRING
DEPOSITS

POROUS ROCK
(sand and gravel)

LAVA FLOWS

STAGE 1

STAGE 2

A GEYSER IN ACTION. Photographs of successive stages in the eruption of Old Faithful illustrate what probably happens during a natural geyser eruption. The underground plumbing is diagrammatic and does not reflect any specific knowledge of Old Faithful's system. Direction of flow of water is shown by arrows. (Based on information supplied by D. E. White, L. J. P. Muffler, R. O. Fournier, and A. H. Truesdell.)

Stage 1 (Recovery or recharge stage). After an eruption, the partly emptied geyser tubes and chambers fill again with water. Hot water enters through a feeder conduit from below, and cooler water percolates in from side channels nearer the surface. Steam bubbles (with some other gases such as carbon dioxide and hydrogen sulfide) start to form in upflowing currents, as a decrease in pressure causes a corresponding decrease in boiling temperature. At first the bubbles condense in the cooler, near-surface water that is not yet at boiling temperature, but eventually all water is heated enough that the bubbles will no longer condense or "dissolve."

Stage 2 (Preliminary eruption stage). As the rising gas bubbles grow in size and number, they tend to clog certain parts of the geyser tube, perhaps at some narrow

80

or constricted point such as at A. When this happens, the expanding steam abruptly forces its way upward through the system and causes some of the water to discharge from the surface vent in preliminary spurts. The deeper part of the system, however, is not yet quite hot enough for "triggering."

Stage 3 (Full eruption stage). Finally, a preliminary spurt "unloads" enough water (with resulting reduction in pressure) to start a chain reaction deeper in the system. Larger amounts of water in the side chambers and pore spaces begin to flash into steam, and the geyser rapidly surges into full eruption.

Stage 4 (Steam stage). When most of the extra energy is spent, and the geyser tubes and chambers are nearly empty, the eruption ceases. Some water remains in local pockets and pore spaces, continuing to make steam for a short while. Thereafter the system begins to fill again, and the eruptive cycle starts anew. (Fig. 50)

81

No two geysers have the same size, shape, and arrangement of tubes and chambers. Also, some geysers, such as Great Fountain, have large surface pools not present in cone-type geysers such as Old Faithful. Hence, each geyser behaves differently from all others in frequency of eruption, length of individual eruptions, and amount of water discharged. Geysers may also vary in their own behavior as their plumbing features change through the years. The great amount of energy that builds up in some of them from time to time creates enough explosive force to shatter parts of the plumbing system, thereby causing a change in their eruptive behavior. In fact, some geyser eruptions have been so violent that large chunks of rock have been exploded out of the ground and scattered around the surrounding area (fig. 51). With time, the precipitation of minerals may partly seal a tube or chamber, gradually altering the eruptive mechanism.

Despite all the variable factors involved in geyser eruptions, and all the changes that can take place from time to time to alter the pattern of those eruptions, several of the Yellowstone geysers function regularly, day after day, week after week, and year after year. Within this group of regulars is the most famous feature of all — Old Faithful — which has not missed an eruption in all the many decades that it has been under close observation (fig. 52). We can only conclude that nature has provided this incredible geyser with a stable plumbing system that is just right to trigger delightfully graceful eruptions at close-enough time intervals to suit the convenience of all Park visitors.

Mudpots

Mudpots are among the most fascinating and interesting of the Yellowstone thermal features. They are also a type of hot spring, but one for which water is in short supply. Whatever water is available becomes thoroughly mixed with clay and other fine undissolved mineral matter. The mud is generally gray, black, white, or cream colored, but some is tinted pale pink and red by iron compounds (fig. 43) ; hence, the picturesque term "paint pots" is commonly used.

Mudpots form in places where the upflowing thermal fluids have chemically decomposed the surface rocks to form

SEISMIC GEYSER, showing rock rubble blown out during an explosive thermal eruption. Note the trees that have been killed by the heat and eruptive activity. According to George D. Marler of the National Park Service, this geyser developed from cracks caused by the Hebgen Lake Earthquake of August 17, 1959. (Fig. 51)

clay. Such small amounts of water are involved, however, that the surface discharge is not great enough to flush the clay out of the spring. Caldrons of mud of all consistencies result, from the very thin soupy material in many mudpots to the almost hard-baked material in the less active features. Some mudpots expel pellets of very thick viscous mud which build up circular cones or mounds; this type is commonly called a "mud volcano" (fig. 53) .

Mudpot activity differs from season to season throughout the year because of the varying amounts of rain and snow that fall upon the surface to further moisten the mud. Accordingly, mudpots are commonly drier in late summer and early fall than they are from winter through early summer.

Fumaroles

Fumaroles (from the Latin word *fumus,* meaning "smoke") are those features that discharge only steam and other gases such as carbon dioxide and hydrogen sulfide; hence, they are commonly called "steam vents." Usually these features are perched on a hillside or other high ground above the level of the flowing springs. In many fumaroles, however, water can be heard boiling violently at some lower, unseen level.

Thermal explosions

A few features present in the Yellowstone thermal areas display evidence that extremely violent thermal explosions occurred in the past, particularly during Pinedale Glaciation, about 15,000 years ago. Such explosion features, of which Pocket Basin in Lower Geyser Basin is a good example, appear as craterlike depressions a few tens of feet to as much as 5,000 feet across surrounded by rims of rock fragments that were blown out of the craters. The underground mechanism causing the explosions was similar to that of geysers, but in these special cases the energy remained bottled-up until a very critical explosive stage was reached.

The best explanation for Pocket Basin and related features is that the ground above the sites of the explosions was weighted down by the water of small lakes which had formed in melted-out pockets of glacial ice. Such localized melting of the glaciers would occur where the ice was in direct contact

◁ OLD FAITHFUL IN FULL ERUPTION. The interval between eruptions averages about 65 minutes, but it varies from 33 to 96 minutes. The time lapse between eruptions can be predicted rather closely, mainly on the basis of the length of time involved in the previous eruption. If an eruption lasted 4 minutes, for example, this means that a certain amount of water emptied from the geyser's chambers and that a certain length of time will be necessary to recharge the system for the next eruption. But if the previous eruption lasted only 3 minutes, less time will be needed for recharge, and the next eruption will occur sooner. (The above discussion is based primarily on many years of observation and study of Old Faithful by George D. Marler and other observers of the National Park Service; photograph courtesy of Sgt. James E. Jensen, U.S. Air Force.) (Fig. 52)

MUD VOLCANO near Pocket Basin in the Lower Geyser Basin. The mud is formed by chemical decomposition of the rocks chiefly by the action of carbon dioxide and sulfuric acid. The splatter, 5–6 feet high, is caused by the escaping gases. (Fig. 53)

with underlying thermal features. A rapid draining of the lake waters would then produce a sudden release of pressure over the hot area, resulting in an unusually violent thermal eruption.

Faulting and its control of thermal activity

Most of the major thermal areas of Yellowstone are related to the ring fracture zones of the Yellowstone caldera (fig. 22). Many deep-seated faults and fractures in these zones are presumably situated above the main source of heat of the thermal system. Thus, they provide convenient avenues of travel for underground waters to circulate to great depths, there to become heated and then rise to the earth's surface (fig. 45). A few areas like Mammoth Hot Springs and Norris Geyser Basin, on the other hand, are not within the ring fracture zones of the caldera. In these areas, the thermal activity is commonly related to other prominent zones of faulting which also afford readymade channelways for the circulation of hot water and steam.

Earthquakes

Earthquakes occur frequently in areas of active faulting and volcanism; they are caused by sudden movements between adjacent blocks of the earth's crust as the crust adjusts to new conditions and pressures. Because of its volcanic history and the fact that very recent fault movements have occurred there, it is not surprising that Yellowstone is an especially active earthquake area. Sensitive instruments (*seismographs*) record an average of about five earth tremors daily in and around the Park, and on rare occasions they may record 100 tremors or more in a single day. Nearly all these tremors are so slight that they cannot be felt by man, but at times, perhaps only once in a human lifetime, one is triggered with high enough intensity to sharply draw our attention to the very real earthquake potential that exists constantly in this geologically active area. Such a high-intensity quake occurred in the Yellowstone region near midnight on August 17, 1959.

The Hebgen Lake Earthquake, as it is known, was centered in the Madison Valley along the west boundary of Yellowstone National Park about 12 miles north of the town of West Yellowstone, Montana (fig. 1). As a result of the quake, a 200-square-mile area, occupied in part by the Hebgen Lake reservoir, subsided a foot or more; maximum subsidence was 20 feet. Movements of several feet along old faults in the highlands along the north side of the valley produced fresh scars several miles long (fig. 54). Moreover, the severe vibrations that rocked the surrounding countryside caused the loose silt, sand, and gravel of the valley floor to slip and become "faulted" in many places. By far the most drastic result was the shaking loose of a huge landslide in the vicinity

EARTHQUAKE DAMAGE. Severe damage caused by reactivation of a fault during the Hebgen Lake Earthquake of August 17, 1959. The building is on the Blarneystone Ranch, about 10 miles north of West Yellowstone, Montana, and 1½ miles west of the west boundary of Yellowstone National Park. (Fig. 54)

of the Rock Creek campground about 25 miles downstream on the Madison River from the west boundary of the Park.

Within Yellowstone National Park, the quake caused only slight damage to buildings at Old Faithful, Mammoth Hot Springs, and a few other places. Small landslides also occurred in various places, for example, at Tuff Cliff near Madison Junction. The earthquake affected many thermal features, particularly those in the main geyser basins near the west side of the Park. In several places the intensity of the thermal activity increased markedly, in fewer places the activity decreased. Some geysers, long dormant, erupted immediately after the earthquake; others erupted with much greater force and frequency than usual; still others became dormant and have remained so. A general, widespread effect was a noticeable increase in the muddiness of many pools and springs, as if the quake had produced a giant surge of water coursing through the underground channels of the geyser basins. Of immediate concern to everyone, of course, was the earthquake's effect on Old Faithful. Fortunately, the only measurable effect was a slight lengthening of time between eruptions. After several months the time interval stabilized at about 65 minutes.

Detailed scientific studies bearing on the Hebgen Lake Earthquake in the weeks that followed showed that it was felt over more than 600,000 square miles of the Western United States, and that it was the strongest shock ever recorded in this part of the Rocky Mountains. In 12 years' time many traces of the quake have disappeared, but its frightful aspects will not soon be forgotten. It serves as a vivid reminder, once again, of the great restlessness that through the ages has been, and continues to be, the very special trademark of the Yellowstone country.

The Park and Man

A hundred years ago another powerful force entered the Yellowstone scene. Man, arriving in ever increasing numbers, came armed with the power to choose between preserving or destroying the wonders that nature has taken more than 2.5 billion years to create. Sensing this grave responsibility, he took the necessary steps to insure that these irreplaceable natural features would be preserved and protected. Today, Yellowstone National Park indeed exists "for the benefit and enjoyment of the people," a fitting and lasting symbol of a great national heritage that now includes more than 275 places of natural and historical interest. On the eve of the 100th anniversary of our first National Park, we are again reminded of that continuing responsibility we all share in preserving these unique places for the benefit and enjoyment of all future generations of visitors.

Acknowledgments

The subject matter of this bulletin is based chiefly on the results of a systematic program of geological investigations in Yellowstone National Park, conducted by the U.S. Geological Survey during the years 1965 – 71. The program, ably organized and directed by A. B. Campbell, required the special skills and knowledge of many individuals to make a comprehensive study of all the varied and complex features of the Park area. Without their invaluable cooperation, assistance, and interest, this endeavor to summarize the geologic story of Yellowstone would not have been possible. I therefore express my sincere thanks to the colleagues listed below, all of whom furnished unpublished information bearing on different aspects of that story: R. L. Christiansen and H. R. Blank, Jr. (Quaternary volcanism) ; H. W. Smedes and H. J. Prostka (Absaroka volcanism) ; D. E. White, L. J. P. Muffler, R. O. Fournier, and A. H. Truesdell (thermal activity) ; G. M. Richmond, K. L. Pierce, and H. A. Waldrop (glaciation) ; E. T. Ruppel and J. D. Love (sedimentary rocks and geologic structure) ; J. D. Obradovich and Meyer Rubin (radiometric dating) . W. L. Newman provided many helpful suggestions regarding the preparation of the manuscript.

The geological studies in Yellowstone received the full support and cooperation of former Park Superintendent J. S. McLaughlin, Superintendent J. K. Anderson, and other personnel of the U.S. National Park Service. In particular, the helpful advice, interest, and enthusiasm of the entire Park Naturalist staff, especially J. M. Good and W. W. Dunmire, former and present Chief Park Naturalists, respectively, greatly facilitated the work in all phases of the program.

90

Selected Additional Reading

Allen, E. T., and Day, A. L., 1935, Hot springs of the Yellowstone National Park: Carnegie Institution of Washington Publication 466, 525 pages.

Boyd, F. R., 1961, Welded tuffs and flows in the rhyolite plateau of Yellowstone Park, Wyoming: Geological Society of America Bulletin, volume 72, number 3, pages 387 – 426.

Christiansen, R. L., and Blank, H. R., Jr., 1972, Volcanic stratigraphy of the Quaternary rhyolite plateau in Yellowstone National Park: U.S. Geological Survey, Professional Paper 729 – B (in press).

Dorf, Erling, 1960, Tertiary fossil forests of Yellowstone National Park, Wyoming, in West Yellowstone — Earthquake area, Billings Geological Society Guidebook 11th Annual Field Conference, 1960: pages 253 – 260.

Hague, Arnold, Iddings, J. P., Weed, W. H., Walcott, C. D., Girty, G. H., Stanton, T. W., and Knowlton, F. H., 1899, Geology of the Yellowstone National Park: U.S. Geological Survey Monograph 32, part 2, 893 pages and atlas of 27 sheets folio.

Hague, Arnold, Weed, W. H., and Iddings, J. P., 1896, Description of the Yellowstone National Park quadrangle [Wyoming]: U.S. Geological Survey Geologic Atlas, Folio 30.

Hayden, F. V., 1872, Preliminary report of the United States Geological Survey of Montana and portions of adjacent Territories, being a fifth annual report of progress — Part I: Washington, U.S. Government Printing Office, pages 13 – 204.

Howard, A. D., 1937, History of the Grand Canyon of the Yellowstone: Geological Society of America Special Paper 6, 159 pages.

Marler, G. D., 1969, The story of Old Faithful: Yellowstone Library and Museum Association, 49 pages.

Richmond, G. M., Pierce, K. L., and Waldrop, H. A., 1972, Surficial geologic map of Yellowstone National Park: U.S. Geological Survey Miscellaneous Geologic Investigations Map I – 710 (in press).

Ruppel, E. T., 1972, Geology of pre-Tertiary rocks in the northern part of Yellowstone National Park, Wyoming: U.S. Geological Survey Professional Paper 729 – A (in press).

Smedes, H. W., and Prostka, H. J., 1972, Absaroka Volcanic Supergroup in the Yellowstone National Park region: U.S. Geological Survey Professional Paper 729 – C (in press).

Smith, R. L., 1960, Ash flows: Geological Society of America Bulletin, volume 71, number 6, pages 795 – 841.

U.S. Geological Survey, 1964, The Hebgen Lake, Montana, earthquake of August 17, 1959: U.S. Geological Survey Professional Paper 435, 242 pages.

U.S. Geological Survey, 1972, Geologic map of Yellowstone National Park: U.S. Geological Survey Miscellaneous Geologic Investigations Map I – 711 (in press).

White, D. E., 1967, Some principles of geyser activity, mainly from Steamboat Springs, Nevada: American Journal of Science, volume 265, number 8, pages 641 – 684.